My Treasury

The Christian Science Publishing Society
210 Massachusetts Avenue, Boston, Massachusetts 02115 USA

My Treasury

ISBN: 978-0-87510-438-6

Printed in USA.

Table of Contents

A Verse
To the Little Children

Mother's New Year Gift to the Little Children

Father-Mother God,
    Loving me,—
Guard me when I sleep;
Guide my little feet
    Up to Thee.

To the Big Children

Father-Mother good, lovingly
    Thee I seek,—
    Patient, meek,
In the way Thou hast,—
Be it slow or fast,
    Up to Thee.

—Mary Baker Eddy

Miscellaneous Writings 1883–1896, p. 400 and *Poems*, p. 69.

A Thank-You Note

Dear God,

So often I take the good things in life for granted. But today I want to let You know how deeply grateful I am to You for all that You've done for me.

Thank you for being my Father and my Mother, for loving me as You do all of Your children. How grateful I am that You have no favorites. I'm not a middle child, the oldest, or the youngest, but just held dear in Your family.

Thank you for providing Your light, which enables me to see what I need to see so that I can make the right choices in any situation.

Thank you for husbanding me—making available to me Your tender, loving, supportive presence in ways that I can see and appreciate. The joy I experience is fresh evidence of Your love in my life. I have learned that joy is mine and can never be taken from me.

Thank you for the blessings of friendship, which I believe is Your way of showing that You care about me.

Thank you for the knowledge that safety isn't the absence of danger but the knowledge of Your presence. It keeps me from harming or being harmed.

Thank you for church. How often it has inspired me, awakened and lifted me out of depression or some other kind of darkness.

Thank you for the many times I've been made whole and free when I've turned to You for help.

Thank you for the gift of gratitude. It brightens every day, softens every thought. It is a grace that continues to grow.

This heart is sincerely grateful to be Your child.

Much love, Me

—Ruth McCleary Truscott

Originally published in the September 4, 2000, issue of the *Christian Science Sentinel*.

You're God's Masterpiece!

Kari always used to be excited about Grandma's visits. She would eagerly gather up her best dolls and favorite books, arrange them just so, and wait for the magical moment when Grandma would join her in the land of make-believe.

But this time, Kari wasn't happy about Grandma coming. Mom was surprised, especially when Kari started saying things that were not so nice about her two-year-old cousin, Michelle. Tears came to Kari's eyes, and she whispered a very sad secret. She was afraid that Michelle had taken her place and that Kari wouldn't be special to anyone anymore. Grandma arrived before Mom could talk to Kari about her feelings. Sadly, Kari told Grandma that her dolls had all run away.

Grandma took her gently into her arms. She said that if there weren't any dolls around today, maybe she and Kari could go to the art museum together. Kari found a little smile, and out the door they went.

Kari had a happy time at the museum. She was especially drawn to the masterpiece paintings of flowers, mountains, trees, streams, birds, and children. When Grandma dropped her off, she wanted to tell Mom all about the paintings, but suddenly her voice broke off with a sigh.

"I guess Grandma will take Michelle to the museum from now on. Michelle's so cute and funny."

While they were at the museum, Mom had prayed, asking God how she could help Kari. Now she had an idea.

"Kari," she said, "let's think about those beautiful paintings. Let's think about the colors, the gardens, the mountains, the birds, the children. Lots of people like to see those paintings because they bring to mind such interesting ideas. That's one reason that the very best paintings are considered masterpieces. Did you ever think you're a masterpiece, too?"

"Me?" Kari asked. "There wasn't any picture of me in the museum!"

"No," Mom said, "but a masterpiece is an important work of art, carefully painted by a brilliant artist. I think the Artist who made you must be especially brilliant."

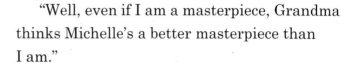

"Well, even if I am a masterpiece, Grandma thinks Michelle's a better masterpiece than I am."

"I think I know why you feel that way. You got tricked into thinking Michelle's Artist is better than yours. But, you have the same Artist! Remember the paintings by Monet that you saw today? They were all painted by the same person, who kept having new and beautiful ideas about the flowers in his garden. Each picture is magnificent, yet each one is different from the rest. They're all masterpieces.

"The Artist who thought of you and Michelle has so many great ideas that He needs both of you to be examples of His thoughts. In fact, He has so many great thoughts that He needs each and every one of us."

"You really mean God, don't you, Mom?" Kari had attended a Christian Science Sunday School since she was very little and had been taught the Bible verse that says, "And God said, Let us make man in our image, after our likeness" (Genesis 1:26).

Mom smiled and said, "You figured it out!"

"The image of God is like a picture, isn't it?"

"Sure, it's like a picture of His thoughts."

"So, God, my Artist, made me especially to be a picture of His thoughts!"

"Right. And the better you know your Artist, the better you know yourself. God makes sure you know you're a masterpiece by telling you something new and delightful about yourself whenever you listen to Him. He tells you something good in the morning, in the afternoon, and at night all the time!"

It made Kari feel better to think that God was telling her something good all the time. Then she had a new idea. "If God is talking to me all the time, then He must be telling Michelle good things about herself, too. She can't take my place, because there isn't room for us to fit in the same masterpiece frame together!" This idea made Kari happy again. It was more fun to think of Michelle in her own picture frame. In fact, Kari thought Michelle was pretty cute, too.

In a few years, when Grandma and Grandpa moved away, Kari and Michelle had wonderful times visiting them together. Kari has discovered that all of God's children are His masterpieces. That means you are, too!

— Shirley T. Paulson

Originally published in the May 10, 1999, issue of the *Christian Science Sentinel*.

What Is God?

Do you ever think about God and wonder what He is like? Do you and your friends sometimes talk about God? Do you ask each other questions because you want to know what God is?

Finding out about God and what He does is very important. For instance, God is Love and He loves us very much. He is always taking care of us. Because we are His children, nothing can hurt us or make us afraid. If we're having a hard time in class, God is there to help. If we're not feeling well, God is there to heal. If we're feeling scared, God is there keeping us safe. We can turn to God in prayer anytime, anyplace, about anything at all. He is with us all the time.

Sometimes we might hear things about God that aren't true. These may make us feel unhappy, even confused. This happened to me. A girl at school told me that God wasn't real. Another said that God is a big old man living up in the sky somewhere, and that He makes us sick when we're naughty. This was scary. It didn't sound or feel right, but I didn't know what else to think. At that time I didn't really know much about God.

Then my grandmother and I went away on a special holiday. When we got to the place we were visiting, she asked me if I would go with her to a Christian Science church. We'd never been to one before. The Church of Christ, Scientist, was started in Boston, Massachusetts, United States of America, by Mary Baker Eddy after she learned about God's healing power. Before she started her Church, she wrote a book about what she had learned and called it *Science and Health with Key to the Scriptures*. My nana, who had been ill for many years, read this book and was healed.

I was so happy about this healing. Nana had been taking medicine for as long as I could remember. Now she was well and had thrown all her medicine away. She said she wouldn't need it again because *Science and Health* told her what God is and how she could rely on Him for healing.

I wanted to know about God, too. That Sunday I went along to the Sunday School. When the lesson time started, the first thing the teacher asked was did I know what God is? I told her I didn't, but I hoped she'd be able to tell me. She said the answers were in the Bible and *Science and Health*.

So we looked up where the Bible tells us that God is Love and that God is Spirit (see I John 4:8, 16 and John 4:24). We also looked in Genesis. Its first chapter says that God created us good, just like Himself (see Genesis 1:26, 27, 31).

Then we looked up the question "What is God?" in *Science and Health* (p. 465). I found that the answer gives seven important synonyms, or names, for God. These helped me understand better what the Bible teaches us about God. For example, God is Spirit, and He makes us spiritual, not material. God is Love, and He causes us to be kind toward others. God is Truth, and He enables us to be honest. God is Life, and so we are full of energy. God is Soul, and He keeps us healthy and happy. God is Mind and Principle. He helps us understand that His laws guide and guard us.

I was so pleased to learn all this about God that I asked Nana if I could keep going to the Sunday School. When we got back home, she asked my mum, who said yes. Shortly after, my mother, brother, and little sister came with us. We all started to read the Bible and *Science and Health* each day. Soon Mum was healed of a bad neck. My brother and sister had healings, too.

I've had lots of healings as well. These healings prove to me that God is good and real. God is ever-present Love, not a person in the sky. He made each of us to be like Him. I know that He never makes us sad or sick. He keeps us safe and well. I'm glad I found out what God is. I'm still learning more and more about Him.

—Beverly Goldsmith

Originally published in the November 22, 1999, issue of the *Christian Science Sentinel*.

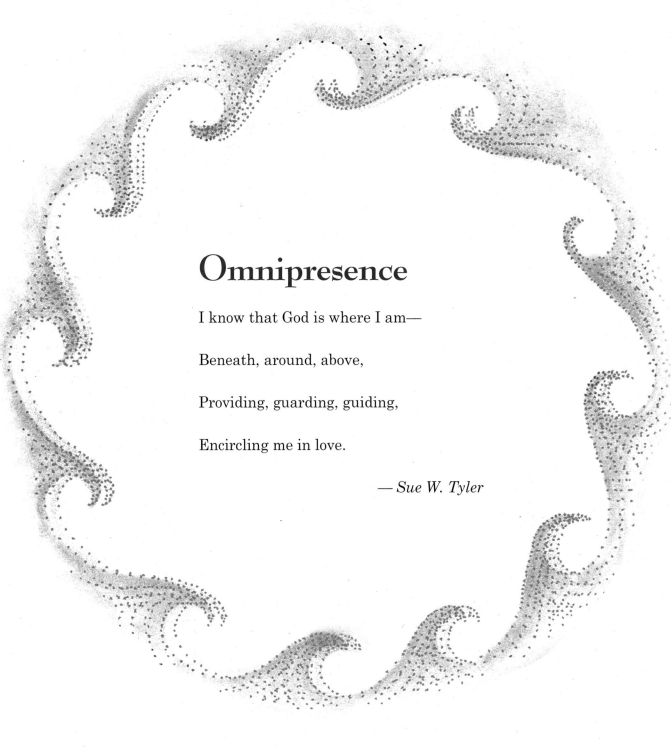

Omnipresence

I know that God is where I am—

Beneath, around, above,

Providing, guarding, guiding,

Encircling me in love.

— *Sue W. Tyler*

Originally published in the December 8, 1951, issue of the *Christian Science Sentinel*.

Illustrated by Bill Oakes

River Rescue

As far as John was concerned, life didn't get any better than this. The Charles River had frozen over behind his friend Steve's house. With the wind in his face and miles of ice to cover, John flew over the ice following his friends.

"Let's skate down to Rocky Narrows!" yelled Steve. But John and Charlie were ready to turn around. Steve skated out of sight as the boys skated away in the opposite direction. Suddenly there was a crunch and a whoosh! Before they knew it, they were in water up to their necks. John's heavy clothes weighed him down as he tried to get a leg up on the ice. Each time he tried to pull on the ice, the edge broke off until the hole grew bigger and bigger. Charlie was having the same problem.

As John tried to catch his breath in the frigid water, he saw the fear on his friend's face. John began to pray. Even as he kept trying to get his leg up and over the edge of the ice, he was also listening hard for God to tell him something. The first thought that came to John was to keep Charlie talking and laughing. John began singing silly songs and Charlie joined in. By the end of one song, each boy had one leg on top of the ice.

Crack! The ice gave way again. They were back in the water, and now the hole was even bigger. That's when John began to pray harder. Charlie prayed too. In a very short time, Charlie managed to pull himself out of the freezing water. He stuck out his hockey stick for John to grab. Within seconds John was out of the water too.

But John didn't stop praying yet. They were still far from home and neither of them could move very well. John prayed a thank-you prayer to God for bringing them this far, knowing that God wouldn't stop caring for him and his friend now. They rested for a moment by the side of the road.

"Hey!" yelled a voice from a car passing on the country road nearby, "What are you guys doing?" It was Steve's older brother.

John quietly thanked God again as the older boy helped carry them to the car. When they pulled into his friend's driveway, there was his mother in their family car! How had she known he needed help? After caring for him and Charlie, and welcoming Steve, who had skated the long way back, Mom and John drove home. She explained that she had felt impelled to drive to Steve's house, knowing there was a need. She always listened for God, divine Mind, in caring for her four children and today was no exception.

John had learned a lesson about not skating on rivers with currents. He had also learned a lot about God's care. God had given him and everyone else all the ideas they needed to keep safe. Father-Mother God had given him songs and prayers with Charlie when he needed them. God had brought Steve's brother, a car, and even his mother waiting with hugs and mugs of hot chocolate. At that moment, John felt the warmth of love surrounding him—love that was God's. He knew for sure that God would always be with him to handle even the toughest situations.

—Sara Hunter

Based on an article originally published in the March 24, 2003, issue of the *Christian Science Sentinel.*

"Be qui-wet! …
and that's good enough"

That's what my three-year-old daughter yelled out the door to our very bouncy, friendly dog. Our dog loved to be exactly where we were at all times. When he couldn't be with us, we kept him right outside the big glass door so he could still see us. But many times that wasn't close enough for him! Then he would bark and bark and *bark*. This time even our little girl drew the line. She ran to the big sliding door, pulled it open with all her might and yelled, "Be qui-wet!" then added very firmly, "and that's good enough."

That's exactly what we need to do with big scary problems. Sometimes problems scream at us just like that barking dog. They yell so loudly that it's hard to hear God's quiet but powerful voice telling us what's really going on, that all is well, that God is Love, and that He is caring for us.

In the book of Psalms, we read, "Be still, and know that I am God" (46:10). We need to slam the door shut on the noisy thoughts so we can hear what God is saying. Christ Jesus taught us how. He said, "When thou prayest, enter into thy closet, and when thou hast shut thy door, pray to thy Father which is in secret; and thy Father which seeth in secret shall reward thee openly" (Matthew 6:6).

You probably have a closet in your room. Maybe you have a secret fort, or a high-up tree house, or a special hide-out in the basement. If so, then you know how it feels to go into your secret place and be all alone in the quiet. It's nice to have a special spot like that. But we don't really need a special *place* closet for us to get quiet because we all have our very own *thought* closet. You can always enter your thought closet and shut the door, even if you're on a noisy playground, at a baseball game, or in the middle of a crowded swimming pool.

Science and Health with Key to the Scriptures explains, "In order to pray aright, we must enter into the closet and shut the door. We must close the lips and silence the material senses" (p. 15). We get quiet by shutting the door on fearful, confused, out-of-control thinking and by instead listening to God's thoughts. God's thoughts are quiet, calm, simple, powerful. They're always good and pure. There's no fear in God's thoughts (they are always thoughts of love). The Bible tells us, "Perfect love casteth out fear" (I John 4:18). God's perfect, loving thoughts wipe out fear-thoughts like a candle wipes out the darkness.

There were many times in the Bible when people had to get quiet in the presence of big or scary problems. I bet you've heard about David and Goliath (see I Samuel, chap. 17.) Goliath was a giant to David and his friends. Goliath's words were giant words: loud, scary, and threatening. He was covered from head to foot with giant armor (the newest, shiniest, best armor). Goliath had everyone's full attention because he was so big and loud and scary.

David was just a shepherd boy. He'd never worn armor before, so he didn't even know how to use it. It certainly seemed that Goliath had all the advantages. He had the size, the experience, the most equipment, and the people's attention. But David listened to God. He remembered how God had taken care of him always. (With God's help, David had been able to protect his sheep from both a lion and a bear.) He also had understanding and trust, courage and faith. These ideas were in his thought closet, so he felt protected and strong. He wasn't afraid as he took his slingshot and five small stones, and ran to meet Goliath.

David's first shot with one small stone hit Goliath right in the forehead (probably the only space *not* covered with armor), and Goliath fell flat. All that big scary fear was gone as quickly as a balloon popping. It really had no power, no strength, no authority, because it had no God or good in it. We can quiet our thought to get rid of Goliath-size fear just as David did.

Once when I was little my family had to do just that. We had a sweet new kitten. She was very tiny, only about eight weeks old. She looked like a little ball of fluff and had the tiniest mew.

One Sunday we put her in the basement before we went to church. When we got home, her "mew" was not tiny at all. Instead it was a loud cry. She had investigated my dad's fishing gear because it smelled like fish. And cats love fish! A small hook from a fishing pole had gone clear through her cheek so that the barb was inside her tiny mouth.

We all sat down on the steps and prayed. Going into our thought closet and turning to God helped us feel Love's presence, the perfect Love that casts out fear. The love of God felt so close, so near, so right there with all of us, that there wasn't any room for fear. Our kitten must have felt this love, too. Whereas before she had been so frightened that we couldn't even hold her still, she now became very quiet and calm, and sat still in my mom's lap.

The kitten stayed quiet while my dad used some tin snips to cut the hook on the outside of her mouth and then gently slip the other piece through on the inside. Then we gave the kitten some warm milk, and she purred loudly and fell asleep. Later we noticed that there was not a single mark on her face. It was as though it had never happened. We still remember that time because of the feeling of God's closeness and the presence of Love that completely cast out fear.

That Love is always with us. We can find it and feel it even in the scariest times. When we feel that Love, all fear disappears. And, that's good enough.

—*Joan Sieber Ware*

Originally published in the May 24, 1999, issue of the *Christian Science Sentinel*.

The Proper Removal of Error

Jim had worked out many problems through Christian Science. He knew that trust in God, his Father-Mother, and the understanding of himself as God's child would solve anything.

One day when he was swimming in a neighbor's pool, a friend noticed sore spots on the bottom of his foot and told him they should be taken off by a doctor because they were ingrown warts. This friend added that he himself had had this condition and that only surgery could help.

Jim told his father about this, and they both agreed that Jim should have help in overcoming the condition. So he went to see a Christian Science practitioner. Although he had often had Christian Science treatment, Jim had never visited a practitioner's office. Now he looked around the cheerful room with much interest. He readily answered the practitioner's questions about his understanding of Christian Science. He told her of several healings he had experienced, and he assured her that he knew the sore spots on his foot could be healed through prayer.

The practitioner asked him to read this passage from the textbook, *Science and Health with Key to the Scriptures* by Mrs. Eddy: "A spiritual idea has not a single element of error, and this truth removes properly whatever is offensive" (p. 463).

Then they talked about the proper removal of anything painful or unpleasant by means of spiritual truths which correct false beliefs about health. Jim could see plainly that it is truth we need, and not operations!

The practitioner asked him, "What is the particular truth which will remove this offensive condition you have come to see me about?"

He thought a few moments; then he said triumphantly, "Why, the truth is that I don't have 'a single element of error,' because I'm God's spiritual idea!"

The practitioner smiled her approval of this answer. She said: "You're right. This is the truth that does the work. Christ Jesus knew this so well that he could heal instantaneously everything that was offensive to men's health and happiness. He always saw God's spiritual idea instead of a sick or unhappy mortal. And he promised that others could do this healing work too."

Together they looked up this verse by Jesus in the Bible, and Jim read it aloud: "He that believeth on me, the works that I do shall he do also; and greater works than these shall he do; because I go unto my Father" (John 14:12).

Jim said thoughtfully, "Well, I believe that." After a few more moments of talking, the practitioner gave him a treatment, as prayer is called in Christian Science, and they said good-bye.

Some weeks later, as Jim was jumping into bed, his father noticed that Jim's foot was completely free of any trace of warts. He asked Jim about this, and Jim said: "Oh, they just fell off the day after I visited the practitioner. You see, we both knew that I am a spiritual idea without anything unpleasant on me. This was all we had to know about the warts. The power of God healed me."

Then Jim wrote this letter to the practitioner:

> *"Dear Friend,*
> *"I am very glad that one day after I saw you I didn't have a sore foot*
> *any more. I am glad that I talked to you. I think talking to you did a lot*
> *for me. Thank you for giving your time to me.*
> *"Love, Jim."*

—Kathryn Paulson Grounds

Originally published in the October 1, 1966, issue of the *Christian Science Sentinel.*

They Vanished Right Before My Eyes

One time I came home from walking our three dogs. I took Oreo, the Chihuahua, upstairs to give her a bath. And I noticed I had quite a few bumps all the way up my arm. It looked like poison oak or poison ivy. My dad and I washed it. The rash and bumps were spreading up my arm quickly; it was scary. Dad shared some thoughts about God with me that helped me not be afraid.

Then we called a Christian Science practitioner. She said that God didn't create skin blemishes or anything that could hurt me. God wouldn't let anything bad, or any error, happen to me. And I thought about this helpful rhyme that the practitioner shared with me: "Error, error, get right out, I've got God to think about." When you're thinking about God, there's no room for fear. The Bible says, "There is no fear in love" (I John 4:18). So I kept thinking that God was protecting me. He loves me unconditionally. And He is always here. I started feeling a lot better.

After I hung up the phone, I watched the bumps vanish right before my eyes.

I hope that rhyme will help you, too!

—Lora Walker

Originally published in the September 3, 2007, issue of the *Christian Science Sentinel*.

In the
Circle of Love

I'm in the circle of Love all day,
Enfolded in God's arms—
Beloved and cared for all the way,
Watched over, safe from harm.

I'm in the circle of Love all day,
No error there to fear—
His angel thoughts are mine always,
Our Father-Mother God is here.

—*Cathrine Joy Hogg*

Originally published in the May 6, 1996, issue of the *Christian Science Sentinel*.

Jessica Lifts Up Her Face "without spot"

Jessica had been practicing every day for her piano recital. She didn't mind practicing because playing the piano was something she really loved to do. Every morning and every afternoon she had practiced, and she felt good about what she was to play.

The day of the recital finally came. The big event wasn't until that evening, but Jessica was excited. She set out her favorite blue dress early in the morning. To try to make the day go by faster, she went out to play in the woods behind her house. She didn't notice that she was playing around the poison ivy.

When Jessica finally went into the house again, she happened to look in a mirror and saw a big red blotch on her face. She was so surprised, and then, so sad. "My recital," she whispered to herself. All she could think about was how this was going to ruin her special evening.

"Everyone will be looking at my face," she cried to her mom, as she showed her the mark on her face. Jessica's mom put her arms around her. The hug felt so warm and comforting. She reminded Jessica that this could be healed through prayer. To some people, that might sound like an amazing thing to say, but not to Jessica. She goes to a Christian Science Sunday School and has learned from experience that the healing Christ Jesus practiced and taught is possible today.

Jessica asked her mom if she could call a Christian Science practitioner. A practitioner is someone who loves and knows the Bible well and prays with you for healing. This

prayer that heals is not a pleading with God to make a bad thing better, but rather a deep conviction and acknowledgment of God's ever-present goodness and constant, loving care for man, His perfect image and likeness.

Jessica liked to call the practitioner herself. It was a special time to her because the practitioner was talking just to her, and she felt so loved. The practitioner told Jessica about a passage in their "lawbook," the Bible. They sometimes called the Bible their "lawbook," because the Bible contains passages that can be looked at and applied like laws in our cities or towns, only these laws are *divine,* from God. The passage reads, "For then shalt thou lift up thy face without spot; yea, thou shalt be stedfast, and shalt not fear" (Job 11:15).

"What a great law, but the piano recital is *tonight,"* Jessica reminded the practitioner.

"God's law is in operation *right now,"* responded the loving but firm voice on the other end of the telephone.

This was like a light in a dark place for Jessica. It was the light of Truth, God, not just words over the phone. Jessica settled back in the chair as she hung up the phone. She just felt so loved. Simply being aware of how much God loved her and how His law of goodness held her safe, even now, made her feel at peace. God is eternal good and holds man, His image and likeness, in that constant goodness. This is a divine law, and it is in effect at any moment—not just at some time in the past or in the distant future!

"By lifting thought above error, or disease, and contending persistently for truth, you destroy error" (p. 400). This is a mighty statement of divine law that Mary Baker Eddy, a devoted student of the Bible and follower of Christ Jesus, was inspired to write in her book *Science and Health with Key to the Scriptures.* And this was exactly what Jessica was doing at that moment—she was lifting her "face," her thinking, above the error, and feeling through and through the stupendous fact that God's law of good is *all* that is going on *all* the time.

Jessica jumped out of her chair. She had things to do. She practiced her piano pieces once again. She helped her mom fix dinner and clean up. Finally, it was time to get ready to go to the recital. She put on her beautiful blue dress and combed her hair. What a thrill it was to look in the mirror and to brush her hair, because her face was completely normal!

That night Jessica played her recital pieces well, with a lot of joy and feeling. How could she not! God's law of goodness and perfection applies to playing the piano, too.

—Stephanie S. Johnson

Originally published in the May 20, 1996, issue of the *Christian Science Sentinel*.

The Secret and Safe Place

Betty was a little girl who had known the protection of Christian Science all of her ten years. From the time she was a baby, the truth had been talked and read to her. When just a toddler she learned to say, "God is Love," and soon after learned the Ten Commandments, the Beatitudes, and the Lord's Prayer with its spiritual interpretation as given in the Christian Science textbook, *Science and Health with Key to the Scriptures* by Mary Baker Eddy. As soon as she was old enough, she went to a Christian Science Sunday School, where she learned more about God and man in His likeness.

Now she was in the fifth grade in grammar school, and this particular day she was hurrying home to tell her mother about something that had happened. The nurse had visited her room the day before and again today, which was unusual, and when she had come this morning, she had looked very grave and announced there was an epidemic in the school. Four cases of a supposedly serious disease had been reported from this one room, and the nurse said she would examine the children every day for the next two weeks.

Mother did not seem alarmed by the report, but neither did she ignore it. She laid aside the work she was doing and reached for her Bible and her Science books, *Science and Health* and *Prose Works* by Mrs. Eddy. "Let's see what protection God has given us," said Mother.

From the Bible she read the ninety-first Psalm, and when she came to the seventh verse, "A thousand shall fall at thy side, and ten thousand at thy right hand; but it shall not come nigh thee," Betty exclaimed, "That must mean that even though the children who sit on either side of me are out of school because of error, it cannot come to me."

Mother agreed, and she read further, "Because thou hast made the Lord, which is my refuge, even the most High, thy habitation; there shall no evil befall thee, neither shall any plague come nigh thy dwelling" (verses 9, 10). Then Mother and Betty talked about what it means to make God our habitation. They knew that a habitation is a dwelling place, a place to live in. Mrs. Eddy says, "Who lives in good, lives also in God,—lives in all Life, through all space" (*Pulpit and Press*, p. 4). To keep our thoughts filled with good and do good is to live in good, and this is to dwell in "the secret place of the most High," to make God our habitation.

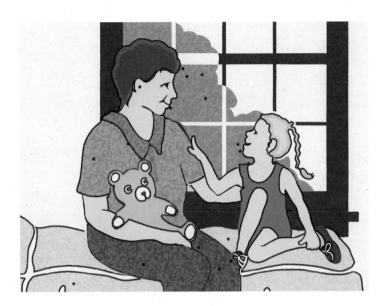

To dwell in a place is to remain there. God's child is not a visitor but a dweller in "the secret place of the most High" (Psalms 91:1). He is not sometimes in danger and sometimes in safety, but always in the presence of God, where no harm can come to him, because man is the idea of God, or divine Mind. Evil cannot enter "the secret place," which is known only to God and His child. Evil can never enter the presence of God.

Christian Science teaches that God is good, and that He is All-in-all. Since good is everywhere, evil can be nowhere. Since good is ever present, filling all space, evil or disease is never present. Only good can come to or go out from God's child.

Betty always read her Bible Lesson early every morning, and then spent a few minutes in turning her thought to God, knowing His ever-presence and all-power, His perfection, and the perfection of His child, made in His image and likeness. Mother pointed out that this, too, was dwelling in "the secret place" and making the Lord our habitation.

Only that morning when Mother had called to her to get ready for school, Betty had been thinking of God's nearness and ever-presence. The good thoughts which came to her were the angels, spoken of in Psalms, which God had given charge over her to keep her in all ways, to uplift and protect her.

Because divine Love is impartial and cares for all with equal tenderness, Betty and Mother knew that in reality no child in the room or the entire school could lack God's protection. It was a help to sing the words from one of Mrs. Eddy's hymns (Hymn 207), "His arm encircles me, and mine, and all." Mother read what our Leader says under the marginal heading "Source of contagion" on page 153 of *Science and Health*, and also her article entitled "Contagion," beginning on page 228 of *Miscellaneous Writings 1883–1896*. Then they sat quietly for a few minutes thanking God for providing the secret and safe dwelling place for His child.

Mother and Betty were happy but not surprised to learn later that not another case of the disease was reported in the entire school, and the four children in Betty's room returned when the quarantine period expired. Thus the epidemic was brought to a halt, and the power of Christian Science to prevent as well as heal disease was demonstrated. "A calm, Christian state of mind is a better preventive of contagion than a drug, or than any other possible sanative method," Mrs. Eddy assures us, adding, "and the 'perfect Love' that 'casteth out fear' is a sure defense" (*Miscellaneous Writings*, p. 229).

—*Evelyn Joy Albright*

Originally published in the December 21, 1946, issue of the *Christian Science Sentinel*.

Keep On Praying!

Tom and his dog were inseparable friends. Jeanie was part collie and part Russian wolfhound. Her long silky fur was all white except for a big brown patch around her left eye.

Tom had no brothers or sisters, but he never felt alone, because he could always play with Jeanie. She kept an eye on Tom wherever they went—to the park, on hikes with Dad in the backcountry, and for rides in the family car. When Tom came home from school, Jeanie ran to him, wagging her tail and yelping happily.

In the fourth grade, Tom and his best friend, George, spent a weekend at Mr. Fullerton's camp in the backcountry. Of course, Jeanie went with the boys. On Sunday morning Mr. Fullerton drove Tom and George into town to go to the Christian Science Sunday School. They left Jeanie alone in a screen porch, and they didn't get back until late afternoon. As they approached the house, Tom cried out, "Look! The porch door is open! Jeanie's not there!"

It looked as if Jeanie had jumped up and released the door latch with her paws. Tom was sure she had run off to find him. They called Jeanie and searched everywhere. Tom was brokenhearted when Jeanie didn't appear.

There were no clues about which direction she might have taken. But there was an important fact that Tom had learned earlier in Sunday School, and he began to pray with it: "God is everywhere." Tom thought that would mean that God was always with each of His creatures. Jeanie could never run away from His love and protection. Tom was sure she would have to be surrounded by God's love, wherever she might be.

The next morning Jeanie was still missing. Tom's dad and mother placed ads in the "lost and found" sections of the local newspapers and contacted the humane society. There were no responses. Days, then weeks passed by. All efforts to find Jeanie were fruitless. For many months no one saw or heard of her. Right from the start an important part of the family's efforts to locate Jeanie was prayer. They felt God was a present help for them, and for her. Tom's mother obeyed the Bible instruction to "pray without ceasing" (I Thessalonians 5:17). Every time she looked at the framed portrait of Tom and Jeanie in the front hall, she silently affirmed that God, divine Mind, is all-knowing. No individuality could ever be lost or separated from its divine source. As ideas of God, she, Tom's father, and Tom all reflected the one divine Mind, which keeps all of its ideas together in perfect harmony. Jeanie, too, was always in the presence of Mind, so Mind knew where Jeanie was, and they could know too. Mother trusted Mrs. Eddy's words, "All of God's creatures, moving in the harmony of Science, are harmless, useful, indestructible" (*Science and Health with Key to the Scriptures*, p. 514).

One of Mrs. Eddy's hymns tells of the "seeking and finding" of Love, and encourages us to "watch and pray" (*Christian Science Hymnal*, No. 207). That's just what Tom and his parents did. They prayed, and trusted God.

Fifty weeks after Jeanie disappeared, Mr. Fullerton telephoned while Tom and Mother were washing the supper dishes. "I think I might have seen Jeanie while I was driving back to camp this evening," he reported. "But when I called her, she ran off into the chaparral."

"We'll come right out!" Tom's father said. "See you in about an hour!"

As they approached Mr. Fullerton's place, they drove slowly, hoping to catch sight of Jeanie. There was no sign of her. The four of them searched the area thoroughly, spreading out, calling Jeanie's name, and shining their flashlights through the low chaparral. There was no response. Disappointed, but not discouraged, Tom thought of the Bible verse, "The effectual fervent prayer of a righteous man availeth much" (James 5:16).

Finally Dad said, "It's getting late. Time to head for town." He knew the backcountry roads well, and decided to drive home by a different route.

As they proceeded slowly along a narrow lane, the car's headlights suddenly shone on a white animal trotting by the roadside. Could it be Jeanie?

Dad pulled the car to the side of the road and turned off the engine. He and Tom got out cautiously and approached the creature slowly so as not to frighten it, softly calling, "Jeanie, Jeanie."

The animal faintly resembled Jeanie. But bony ribs stood out through matted and dirty fur. Instead of Jeanie's leather collar and license, there was just a frayed rope dangling.

Over the past eleven months Tom had grown taller, and his voice was different. The dog did not recognize him and shied away, about to disappear into the darkness. Tom thought, "It must not be Jeanie after all."

Then he caught a glimpse of the big brown patch around the dog's left eye. It must be Jeanie! But still she showed no sign of recognition. How could they convince her?

Before, when he played with Jeanie, Dad would take his walking stick and wave it at her. It was her favorite kind of roughhouse. Now Dad raised his walking stick over his head in the familiar gesture—an invitation to play. Immediately the dog responded. She bounded forward, her tail wildly wagging. It *was* Jeanie.

Nobody ever knew what hardships Jeanie had endured during her long absence from home, but the months of separation were quickly forgotten. Tom and Jeanie resumed their close companionship. And the family always thanked God that they had learned to keep on praying.

—Paul Hofflund and Anne M. Hofflund

Originally published in the November 2, 1987, issue of the *Christian Science Sentinel*.

What Can I Do With My Grateful Thoughts?

There must be a way to say "thank you" to God
　　for all of the good He is giving.
And surely today a wonderful way
　　is to see that my "thank-you" I'm *living*.

It's not just the words that I say when I'm glad
　　or only the good thoughts I'm knowing.
To *tell* God I'm thankful is not quite enough;
　　I've got to be sure that it's showing!

When Mommy is carrying groceries inside
　　or Daddy is washing his car,
or Sister needs help when she's tying her shoe,
　　I can *prove* what my grateful thoughts are.

By helping my sister and mother and dad
　　I'm able to show how I feel.
My gratefulness then blesses others as well,
　　and I know that *this* "thank-you" is real!

—*Beverly Jean McCreary*

Originally published in the March 28, 1983, issue of the *Christian Science Sentinel*.

How Forgiveness Heals

Forgiving isn't so hard to do when we realize
that nothing can force us to hate or hurt someone else,
since we are all truly the children of God, Love. Matt had two
experiences proving that forgiveness, not anger or revenge, leads to healing.

Matt was helping his dad mow the grass. There always seemed to be pastures to cut in the summer. He didn't mind, because he got to drive the lawn tractor, and that was fun. One afternoon, though, while cutting grass, the mower went over a nest of yellow jackets. The startled insects swarmed all over Matt, stinging him in many places. His dad carried him into the house to his mom.

Matt's parents checked him and his clothing for more yellow jackets and removed them. While they did so, they talked with him about God's tender, constant love for all His creation. This love included not only Matt, but also the yellow jackets. God is Love. And God and His love aren't limited. God doesn't take love from one of His precious ideas in order to give to another—His love for all is infinite. In fact, the infinite Love that is God is a protection from anything harmful. So, really, nothing had hurt Matt, because God's infinite, protecting love had been surrounding him all the time.

This thought gave Matt hope, despite the swelling and pain. Even though the stings hurt, Matt knew he needed to turn completely to God to help him. God gave him the answer right away. It was, "You must forgive the yellow jackets."

At first this sounded impossible. But when Matt shared this idea with his folks, they explained that without forgiveness it would be hard to make progress and see healing. They said that being resentful was like holding a hot coal in your fist. As long as it was there, it would continue to burn your hand. The only way to stop the burning was to let go of the coal.

In Sunday School, Matt had learned the Lord's Prayer, given to the world by Christ Jesus (see Matthew 6:9–13). One part reads, "And forgive us our debts, as we forgive our debtors." In *Science and Health with Key to the Scriptures*, Mary Baker Eddy gives what she understands is the spiritual sense of the Lord's Prayer. About forgiving it says, *"And Love is reflected in love"* (p. 17).

Matt thought, "If God loves me no matter what, and I express God's love, then *I* must love no matter what. I have to love and forgive the yellow jackets, because God also loves them." As Matt worked with this idea of forgiveness, the pain stopped. He could see he was on the right track. He was learning to let go of the burning coal.

His mom suggested that he study the Beatitudes in the Bible. One really stood out to him. It said, "Blessed are the merciful: for they shall obtain mercy" (Matthew 5:7). It seemed to him that mercy and forgiveness were a lot alike. He thought about how mercy and forgiveness could bring healing. Then he understood! By forgiving the yellow jackets he was denying that there could be anything harmful in God's creation. He was expressing God's unconditional love for all His creatures. And, he was celebrating the fact that as God's reflection, he was really spiritual, not material.

Working with these ideas and trusting God to see him through this, Matt was healed of all evidence of stings.

He didn't forget this lesson, either. More recently, when he was petting his cat, Woolfie, the cat reached up to pat Matt's face. His claw stuck inside Matt's nose, causing a lot of bleeding. Instead of getting angry and upset with Woolfie, Matt picked him up and comforted him (Woolfie seemed upset at what had happened). Almost instantly the bleeding stopped. Matt knew that by not reacting, he had expressed the Christly quality of forgiveness, and this ended the problem.

Matt learned that forgiveness really does bring healing.

—*Kathleen J. Wiegand*

Originally published in the August 9, 1999, issue of the *Christian Science Sentinel*.

About Lamps

I remember hearing of a little church in Switzerland which had no lighting equipment; so when the villagers wanted to have a service after dark, each took his own light. It was a pretty sight when they all got together, and when there was a large congregation the lights were very bright.

This custom of each tending his own light reminds me of Jesus' words in the Sermon on the Mount (Matthew 5:14), "Ye are the light of the world," and (verse 16), "Let your light so shine before men, that they may see your good works..." Through man God brings light to the world because man reflects God. What a lovely thought to take to church and to Sunday School! For the light which Jesus was talking about was the light of Mind. It is the same light which we sing about in the verse that runs:

> O Spirit, source of light,
>   Thy grace is unconfined;
> Dispel the gloomy shades of night,
>   Reveal the light of Mind
>   (*Christian Science Hymnal*, No. 240).

Christian Science shows us how to reflect light—the light which chases away the darkness of fear, sin, pain, and unhappiness. Sometimes darkness seems big and frightening, and yet a lighted candle can disperse most of it, and a lighted lamp still more. So as we go on learning to reflect more and more of the light of Love, the light of Truth, the light of Life, we shall find that error will disappear.

Have you ever noticed how quietly light does its work? There is no fuss, no noise, no struggle. Just light and more light, and the darkness vanishes. So error fades away into nothingness before the light of God. All we have to do is to remember that man is God's reflection, and then let our light shine more and more until the darkness disappears.

And let us remember that a lamp needs three things: first it needs oil, for it cannot burn at all without oil; then its wick must be kept trimmed and clean, otherwise there will be a black smoke instead of a bright light; and, last, the glass which the light shines through must be polished until it is bright and clear.

In *Science and Health with Key to the Scriptures,* Mary Baker Eddy tells us that *oil* means "consecration; charity; gentleness; prayer; heavenly inspiration" (p. 592). So these, are the qualities which keep our lamps burning and drive away the darkness of fear. "Consecration" is a big word, but it means we have to put God first, to love Him enough to be patient and careful, faithful and obedient, and persevering. Charity is another name for love. And we all know what gentleness and prayer are. Heavenly inspiration is the joyous understanding which comes to us when we are close to God.

The Israelites must have felt close to God when the plague of darkness came, for we read that though there was darkness over the land, a darkness so great it could be felt, "the children of Israel had light in their dwellings" (Exodus 10:23).

One little girl who always dreaded the time when she went to bed because the room was dark, began to understand that she could have light in her dwelling, her thoughts, by reflecting love and gentleness. Then the fear left her, and she felt the light of Love all around her.

The wicks in our lamps are trimmed and clean if there are no thoughts of error to cause a fog and keep our light from shining. Our glass is bright when our reflection of God is so clear that others can see the light.

One little boy always dreaded going back to school. Sometimes this dread of going back made him ill. One day he told his fear to his Sunday School teacher. Together they saw that, just as a car sends a bright beam from its headlights along the road it is going to travel, so we, when faced with a fear of something to come, can fill our thoughts so full of the light of Truth and Love that the beam will shine out far ahead of us and all the way will be bright. David did this and found happiness the next time he had to go back to school. You see, the light shone on the path before him, and there was no error to meet by the time he got there.

When our lamps are lighted and burning brightly, we shall not be afraid. Best of all, others will be helped by seeing the light of Love which we express.

—Gwendolen A. Mitchell

Originally published in the April 13, 1946, issue of the *Christian Science Sentinel*.

The Church that Children Built

This is the church that the kids built in 1898. It was in Schofield, Wisconsin. Too bad it's not there anymore.

Do you know the Bible verse that says, "And a little child shall lead them" (Isaiah 11:6)? Over 100 years ago some children in Schofield, Wisconsin, United States, demonstrated this perfectly. In the 1890s Schofield was a logging town made up of sawmills of the Brooks and Ross Lumber Company, the homes of the employees, and a post office. In this town 18 children, from 8 to 16 years old, did something amazing: They held their own Christian Science church services and built their own church.

The First Reader of this church was Mary Graves, a student of Mary Baker Eddy's and the only adult. The Second Reader was Florence Harney, a 14-year-old. The clerk was 16-year-old Edith Harney, and the treasurer was Alfred Glarson, also 14. Alfred recorded each and every collection.

In October 1898, they discovered that the church had an extra nine dollars. The children held a meeting and decided to appoint a building committee and build a new church. (A building committee plans for everything that's needed for a building.) Today, we probably wouldn't decide to build a church if we had only nine dollars. But in the 1890s nine dollars was worth a lot more, so you could buy more with it.

Within two days, someone donated a place to build the church. Another person donated ten dollars. And a grateful person who had been healed through Miss Graves's prayers donated 25 dollars.

The building committee then went to Mr. Brooks at the lumber company and asked if they could buy lumber at a reduced rate. They thought they would only put in the foundation of their building that winter. But Mr. Brooks encouraged them to build the church sooner, and advised them to build a bigger building than they had planned.

In about two months, the church was completed. It was called First Church of Christ, Scientist, Schofield. The seating limit was 100.

And on the day of dedication, it was completely filled. Even people from out of state came.

I think it's cool that children can have enough spiritual motivation to want to have a church and a service, so that they can practice Christian Science together. And it doesn't matter if there's only one adult helping. You just need to love Christian Science and want to be part of it. I think that these kids are a wonderful role model, because they show that it doesn't matter that you are young. You can still participate in a big way.

— Camille Richardson

Originally published in the August 14, 2006, issue of the *Christian Science Sentinel*.

Catch the Spirit!

It was Bucky's second summer in Little League baseball, and he really loved the game. One particular day, however, before practice, he looked unusually sad and quiet.

"Why the long face, pal?" his dad asked. "It looks as if you lost your last friend!"

"I just don't seem to be any good at baseball," replied Bucky. "I haven't had a hit all season, and the coach will only put me in right field. That's where they put all the crummy players, you know! Besides, we hardly ever win a game, and it just doesn't seem like much fun anymore."

"Come with me. I want to show you something," said Dad. He led Bucky to the front of the large mirror that hung over his dresser. "Look in the mirror and tell me what you see."

As Bucky looked at his reflection in the mirror, a smile began to beam across his face. He remembered something his granddad used to do. It all started with Granddad telling them of a lake Mary Baker Eddy writes about in *Science and Health with Key to the Scriptures* (see p. 477). It's one that North American Indians called "the smile of the Great Spirit." Bucky's granddad had told him that the Indian name for it was Winnipesaukee (Win-a-pa-SOCK-ee). It was such an unusual-sounding name! When any of his grandchildren were sad, Granddad would sit them in front of the mirror and have them repeat aloud, "Win-a-pa-SOCK-ee!" five times in a row. Nobody had ever made it five times without laughing.

"Winnipesaukee, the smile of the Great Spirit!" Bucky called out as he looked in the mirror.

Dad and Bucky both had a big laugh, and then they began to talk about what "the smile of the Great Spirit" means. Bucky had learned in the Christian Science Sunday School that God is Spirit, and since God made each one of His children in His image and likeness, each one truly is His perfect, spiritual reflection—or, you might say, His "smile," His expression. Now, Bucky had learned that God is also Principle, Mind, Life, Truth, Soul, Love. In fact, that sentence from *Science and Health* that Granddad told Bucky about says: "Man is the expression of Soul. The Indians caught some glimpses of the underlying reality, when they called a certain beautiful lake 'the smile of the Great Spirit'" (p. 477).

As Bucky and his dad talked, Bucky discovered that playing baseball gave him a wonderful opportunity to express God. By obeying the rules of the game and by never cheating, Bucky wasn't just playing fair, he was being law-abiding and expressing Principle.

By his alertness on the field, his better and better judgment of where the ball would go, and the perception that made him able to hit the ball at just the right time, he expressed Mind. Through his energy and joy, his ability to see, hear, move well, he expressed Spirit, Soul. Life could be seen in health, freshness, and safety. These qualities of God are always expressed in His child. Dad explained to Bucky that accuracy, precision, and correctness—all important in baseball—were his as the reflection of Truth. And of course, last but not least, being kind to teammates and opponents is not just showing good sportsmanship; it's expressing Love, as Christ Jesus taught us to do.

As the time for Little League rolled around, Bucky really looked forward to putting into practice what he had just learned. When the team was doing infield practice and Bucky took his turn, he didn't miss fielding a single ball! And he was hitting during batting practice. Best of all, he was encouraging and praising his teammates. Neither Bucky nor his dad was surprised when, on game day, they overheard one coach tell the other, "I think we should play Bucky in the infield today."

As the kids ran onto the field, one could actually sense a change taking place. It started with one, then two, until the whole team seemed to have caught a wonderful new feeling. Each player was shouting words of encouragement to the others, and everyone was working together as a team should.

When Bucky's team came to bat, the encouragement, the teamwork, continued. Bucky even got his first game hit! As the runs started to come in and the opposing team began to show signs of discouragement, Bucky's team began to encourage *them*—to cheer for them when a good play was made and to applaud them when they got a clean hit. Before long, it spread into the stands. You couldn't tell which parent was rooting for which team! All the parents were encouraging all the kids. No "boos" or harsh words.

By the end of the game, no one but the scorekeeper knew who had "won"—or cared! The scorekeeper did say the entire game was played without a single error being committed by either side.

—*Wayne L. Bart, Jr.*

Originally published in the January 23, 1995, issue of the *Christian Science Sentinel*.

Back to Toowoomba

During the school holidays several young Australian boys decided to hike through bushland to a favorite picnic spot called "The Seven Mile Caves." It was seven miles from their hometown of Toowoomba.

They set out bright and early one morning and had a day of exploring caves, swimming in the clear, cold stream, cooking their midday meal over a smoky fire, and swinging on monkey-ropes from tree to tree. When it was time to go home, they were careful to put out the campfire and gather their belongings. Then they set out.

But the return journey seemed a long way, and when one of the boys said he knew of a much shorter track, they let him take the lead.

After tramping a long time, they were no nearer the main road into town. In fact they were lost. The boys sank down under a tree to rest. They were hot and thirsty and by now a little afraid. It was growing late and the evening shadows were already lengthening. Soon it would be dark, and their parents would probably be getting anxious.

Two of the boys were brothers and attended a Christian Science Sunday School. Before they left home that morning, their mother had reminded them of the ever-presence of their loving Father-Mother God. To assure them of their perfect safety throughout the day, she read to them these two verses from a favorite psalm: "The Lord shall preserve thee from all evil.... The Lord shall preserve thy going out and thy coming in from this time forth, and even for evermore" (Psalms 121:7, 8).

So now, feeling tired and scared, the brothers reminded each other of these truths, that as children of God they had never been out of His loving presence, because in Him they lived, and moved, and had their being (see Acts 17:28), as the Bible says. This same good God is Mind and knows all things. As spiritual man is a reflection of Mind, he knows everything necessary.

They suddenly remembered a sentence they had often read from the Christian Science textbook, *Science and Health with Key to the Scriptures* by Mary Baker Eddy, "Love inspires, illumines, designates, and leads the way" (p. 454). Also they recalled these lines by Mrs. Eddy from a hymn: "Shepherd, show me how to go / O'er the hillside steep" (*Christian Science Hymnal*, No. 304).

By now they felt more cheerful, and after a few minutes it occurred to them to climb a high tree and look for a familiar landmark. From the top of a tree one of the bigger boys saw an electric light pole not too far away. They soon reached it, and by following the overhead line, in a short time came to the main road about ten miles from town. They trudged along the road until they reached a service station where the two brothers could phone their mother to come and pick them all up in the car.

The boys waited in the shelter of the service station and sipped a cool drink the owner gave them. They soon got over their weariness, and when the family car appeared on the scene, they couldn't scramble into it quickly enough.

The boys' mother thanked the owner of the service station for his kindness, and the boys soon ate all the fruit she had brought for them. They sang all the way home in the car. When the other boys had been delivered to their different homes, the two brothers had a warm bath and an extra good supper. When their father came home, they told him their story, and they all agreed it was God's love that made them stop being afraid and led them to safety. They'd had a real adventure!

—*Janet McIntyre*

Originally published in the May 29, 1976, issue of the *Christian Science Sentinel*.

Standing on the Rock

There were five children in Marie's family, and she was right in the middle. She had two older sisters and a younger sister and brother. She liked to think of herself as one of the big kids with her two older sisters. Her brother and little sister were the little kids. But being one of the big kids meant that she had to help with the chores. Washing dishes after dinner, drying and putting them away, and feeding the cats were everyday chores the big kids took turns with. On Saturday everyone cleaned house.

One day, when it was Marie's turn to feed the cats, she opened a new can of cat food for a special treat and took it outside to the cats' bowls. The sharp lid of the can fell on the ground and somehow got caught between Marie's bare feet and cut both of her heels. The cuts hurt and started bleeding a lot.

Dad had just come home from work, so she called for him. When things went wrong, Marie would often call her dad to come and talk to her about Truth. Marie's family went to the Christian Science church, and in Christian Science, *Truth* is a name for God. It is written with a capital *T* to show when it means God, who is the only power. God is eternal, and so divine Truth is much more than just an idea we think is right or some fact we've read in a book. Truth with a capital *T* was Marie's favorite way to think of God. Real

Truth can't be changed or argued away. And Christ Jesus, through all of the healing that he did, showed us that we can be completely sure of Truth.

Dad came out, and as he began cleaning up her feet, he noticed that she was feeling even more scared. He said maybe she shouldn't look at her heels anymore. This wasn't just so she would forget about getting cut, but so she could think more clearly about what was really true about her as God's child.

Marie knew that our eyes can't see Truth—we can't see God with our material eyes—because God is Spirit. And since we are made by God to be like Him, we must be spiritual. So our eyes really can't see the true man, either. Marie knew that to see the true man she would need to listen to God speaking to her thoughts, and she would not need to inspect her heels.

Dad knew, too, that Truth had laws that couldn't be broken, and that there were no exceptions. Because Truth is good and is no accident, nothing has any power to overcome good. Dad put neat bandages on Marie's heels and noticed that they weren't bleeding anymore.

The next day Marie wore sandals that didn't rub to school, and she didn't think much about the cuts until one of them started bleeding again when she was running around at recess. This time she wasn't afraid. She went to the edge of the playground and remembered the ideas that she and Dad had talked about the night before. And this time she really felt secure and safe with Truth.

Feeling God's presence in a situation like this is something like standing on a big rock. David, who wrote many of the psalms in the Bible, said about God, "He only is my rock and my salvation: he is my defence; I shall not be moved" (Psalms 62:6).

Mary Baker Eddy, who discovered Christian Science, lived at one time near the northeast coast of the United States.

The shore there is rocky and rough in many places. And the winter storms are rough. The ocean waves often break on the rocks, and storms can send the waves crashing and splashing high into the air—way over our heads. But the rocks don't move. Maybe Mrs. Eddy was thinking about those rocks when she wrote the words in one of the hymns in the *Christian Science Hymnal* (No. 253):

> Thus Truth engrounds me on the rock,
> Upon Life's shore,
> 'Gainst which the winds and waves can shock,
> Oh, nevermore!

No matter how scary something seems, when we stand on Truth, we are unmoved— unafraid of anything that tells us we could be hurt. We know we are safe in God's care.

Marie didn't think about all of this on the playground. But she did feel safe and secure with God, Truth. She told her friends that she was OK and cleaned up her foot by herself.

And after that, Marie didn't think much about the cuts. She didn't wear bandages anymore, and there weren't any scars either. But there were plenty of other times that she and her father talked about Truth, because Truth seemed more and more important to them all the time.

—*Nancy Hormel Reinert*

Originally published in the April 6, 1992, issue of the *Christian Science Sentinel*.

Father-Mother God

When I was a baby, I relied totally on my mom and dad for everything. They cared for me, fed me, and clothed me. When I got older and was a student in Sunday School, I learned that I could turn as completely and as confidently to God, the Father and Mother of us all, as I had to my parents when I was little. More and more I found myself turning to God whenever I felt I needed the strength of my Father and the loving tenderness of my Mother. My mom and dad understood this relation to God, too. They encouraged me to trust Him completely, to know that God made me and always loves and cares for me completely.

Once, when I was 12 years old, my little brother began to feel quite ill in the middle of the day. He went into the house without telling anyone and got into his bed. We shared the bedroom, and I noticed him lying there when I came into the house to get something. I asked him if he was OK. He said that he was really feeling bad. He didn't want to eat anything, didn't want to get out of bed, and didn't even want to go out and play with his friends.

I had been learning about God as my Father-Mother. I had also learned that praying to God brings answers to any problem, anytime, anywhere. So, while I told my parents about this later in the day, at the time I just turned to God.

I talked with my brother about God. I told him that God loved him and could heal him. Then I got my copy of *Science and Health with Key to the Scriptures*, and I read to him parts I felt would be good for him to hear. I don't remember the exact passages I read, but I do know that the sense of God as my brother's Father-Mother was in my heart, and I wanted him to feel that way, too.

The people who wrote the Bible mostly thought of God as our Father, but Mrs. Eddy

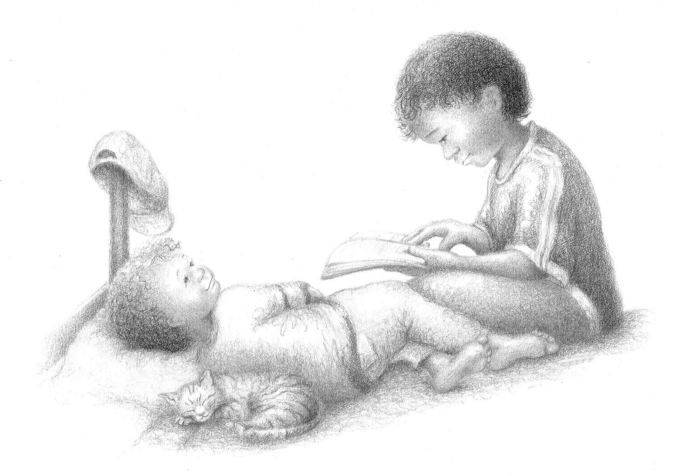

thought of God as Father-Mother and often referred to God this way. On page 332 of *Science and Health*, she writes, "Father-Mother is the name for Deity, which indicates His tender relationship to His spiritual creation."

God created man in His image and likeness—good like God: "And God said, Let us make man in our image, after our likeness: and let them have dominion over … all the earth" (Genesis 1:26).

My Sunday School teacher had told me to think of the "us" in this passage as Father-Mother God. This meant a great deal to me, because I began thinking of God in a much more complete way than just my Father. I thought of all of the wonderful ways my mom expressed motherhood, and I realized that God was all those things and more. I began to understand God as tender, loving, and sensitive to my needs and to the needs of all of Her creation. I thought of the strength and courage of my dad. Then, I recognized that God was infinite strength, courage, and support. It helped me understand that patience, gentleness, and caring were not exclusively "girl" qualities. Nor were strength, courage, and persistence exclusively "boy" qualities.

I learned that the wonderful qualities I saw in my parents came from our Father-Mother, God. This didn't cause me to love my mom and dad any less. In fact, it caused me to love them more, in a purer, more spiritual way. I also saw that I contained all of these qualities, and so did my brother and all of my friends and teachers—actually so did everybody in the world! Knowing these facts, I could see my brother as God's child.

To my surprise, after only a short amount of time and while I was still reading to him, my brother looked up at me and said, "I feel OK, now. I think I am going to go outside to play." And he did.

I was so filled with a sense of wonder, gratitude, and inspiration that I went on reading and soaking up the thoughts I was receiving for quite a while after he went outside. I forgot all about what I had come into the house to get. I even forgot about going back outside to play. I felt, and may even have said out loud, "Thank you, Father-Mother."

Knowing that our Father-Mother had made my brother perfect, and loved him, completely healed him and enabled him to hop up and run outside to play. I couldn't wait to tell my Sunday School class that I had proved what we were learning about God, our divine Parent.

—Don LeRoy Griffith III

Originally published in the June 7, 1999, issue of the *Christian Science Sentinel*.

Guarded While Asleep

Now I lay me down to sleep.
My Shepherd will protect and keep
Me safely from all fears and harms,
Cuddled closely in His arms.
I will sleep in peace, throughout the night
And wake refreshed, with the morning light.

— *Phyllis Hayes Colman*

Originally published in the March 23, 1998, issue of the *Christian Science Sentinel*.

No Monsters

Andrew came into his parents' bedroom one night after he had already been tucked into bed and said that he was afraid of the monsters in his bedroom. Mommy told him that he should shut monsters out of his thoughts and instead think about the loving presence of God right there with him. She reminded him of the happy time he had had that day with friends at the park and the zoo, and said he should think about these good things and be grateful to God. Andrew went back to his room and turned on his light and was talking to himself.

After giving him several minutes alone, Mommy went in to check on him. As she went down the hall, she could hear him saying: "There are no monsters. God is Love, and His love is right here around me."

Andrew was sitting on his bunk bed with *Science and Health with Key to the Scriptures* and a globe. He had gotten out *Science and Health* because he knew it told him about the all-powerful presence and goodness of God; it also told him about the nothingness of error, or evil. Even though he couldn't yet read all of the words in this book, Mommy had read to him from it many times, and he knew the comforting truth was in it.

But why had he brought the globe into his bed? When Mommy asked him about this, he said, "Because I was saying that there are no monsters *anywhere* in the world." Mommy said that she was proud of him for praying for the whole world.

Andrew was praying by denying that monsters are real and affirming that God was right there with him, keeping him safe all the time. Denying is like saying "no" to a bad suggestion or request or demand. Affirming is the opposite of denying. It's like saying to a good thought, "Yes, I know this is true because God tells me it is."

Andrew said, "You know, Mommy, when I said that there were no monsters, the monsters disappeared." Mommy said, "Yes, that's because they were never really there." After putting away the globe and the book and turning out the light, she quietly sang to him the hymn, "Feed My Sheep" (*Christian Science Hymnal*, No. 304). The comforting words were written by Mary Baker Eddy. The third verse reads:

So, when day grows dark and cold,
Tear or triumph harms,
Lead Thy lambkins to the fold;
Take them in Thine arms;
Feed the hungry, heal the heart,
Till the morning's beam;
White as wool, ere they depart,
Shepherd, wash them clean.

When Mommy kissed Andrew good night, he had a smile on his face and felt snug and safe in his bed. He slept peacefully the whole night.

We might see monsters or make-believe creatures on television or read about them in books,

but it's so important not to think that they are real or that they have even a tiny place in God's creation. One dictionary says a monster is like a hideous evil or wrong. So it doesn't really matter what we imagine a monster to be like. We can always know, if it's evil or makes us feel afraid, it never was and never can be a part of what God, good, makes. More important, it can't stop us from knowing that God is with us.

Later when Andrew and Mommy were talking, he said: "Sometimes if I still feel afraid, I pray and say, 'There are no monsters.' And I feel God's presence with me. Then I don't even have to turn on the light or anything. I can just go to sleep."

The Bible say: "God is love; and he that dwelleth in love dwelleth in God, and God in him. ... There is no fear in love; but perfect love casteth out fear" (I John 4:16, 18).

—*Joy L. Nack*

Originally published in the January 5, 1998, issue of the *Christian Science Sentinel*.

Take Off Those Green Glasses

Do you know the story of the Wizard of Oz? Dorothy and her friends go to the Emerald City to get help from the wizard. Before they get there, they have to put on green glasses. When they enter the city, everything looks emerald green. It isn't until much later in their adventures that Dorothy and the others take off their glasses and see the city as it really is. Of course, when they do that, they discover it isn't green. The glasses had just made everything look green. The glasses created an illusion, which is something that seems to be but isn't.

The Wizard of Oz is a good story. It's funny to think of how all the characters have been fooled. In real life, though, you don't want to be tricked into believing something that's not true. But how can you be sure what is true and what isn't?

Well, the Bible can help us. In Genesis, the first book of the Bible, there are two different accounts of how God created man. In the first, God makes man—all of us—in His image and likeness. That means that God, who is perfect Spirit, makes us perfect and spiritual, like Himself. In the second story, God makes a man, Adam, out of dust, and then uses one of his bones to make a woman, whom Adam names Eve.

Jesus' teachings show that the first account is the true one. He once said, "Be ye therefore perfect, even as your Father which is in heaven is perfect" (Matthew 5:48). Being perfect is being Godlike. Only God's image and likeness could be that way. A man made from dust could never be perfect like God. So I think Jesus was telling us we are actually spiritual, not the skin and bones we seem to be.

One time when I got hurt, I had to be careful not to accept the illusion that I was skin and bones. I was having a good time, walking in a large field. As I went through a gate where there were lots of rocks, my foot turned and something snapped. My foot began to hurt, and it was hard to walk.

As I prayed about this, I thought about what was really true about me. The pain in my foot seemed to be shouting, "You've had an accident and been hurt!" But I knew that if God, who is perfect, made me in His image and likeness, I was just as perfect as could be. Because I am actually spiritual, not skin and bones, no part of my real being could be broken or out of place.

I also thought about the fact that God is Love. And because He made me, loves me, and is always taking care of me, He would never let me be hurt. So believing that the accident and pain were true would be like looking through green glasses instead of seeing things the way God made them, which is the way they really are.

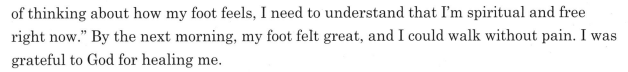

I kept walking and praying for the rest of the day. Even though my foot still hurt, I kept arguing, "No, this accident can't affect me. I'm not a skin-and-bones girl but the perfect child of God. Instead of thinking about how my foot feels, I need to understand that I'm spiritual and free right now." By the next morning, my foot felt great, and I could walk without pain. I was grateful to God for healing me.

The book *Science and Health with Key to the Scriptures* by Mary Baker Eddy talks about illusions. It states, "When the illusion of sickness or sin tempts you, cling steadfastly to God and His idea" (p. 495). If we keep thinking about God and clinging to God, any illusions of pain or trouble will be destroyed.

So, if you're faced with a problem, you can ask yourself, "Is this true, or am I looking through green glasses and seeing an illusion?" You'll know it's true if it's good, like God. If it's not, then it's actually an illusion. Take off those green glasses and discover what's really true about you.

— *Lois Sauer Degler*

Originally published in the February 28, 2000, issue of the *Christian Science Sentinel*.

Shea's New School

Shea loved her new house. She and her friend Kate could run and tumble in all its big rooms. But Shea wasn't so happy with her new school.

It was the middle of the school year, and the first-grade reading class was several books ahead of her old school. Her mom would sit with her at home and try to go over the words, but Shea didn't even want to think about them. In class she couldn't understand the lessons and felt stupid and afraid. Her teacher was sad to give her low grades.

One morning Shea's mom stopped by to see Kate's mom. In the pretty blue and yellow kitchen, the moms talked. "Shea is miserable at her new school," her mom said. "Why, this morning she cried and didn't even want to get on the bus."

Kate's grandmother was reading at the table nearby. When she heard about Shea, she went quietly to her room and shut the door.

Grandma prayed. She knew that children's thoughts are pure and close to God's goodness. She recalled reading in the Bible about the time when Jesus gathered the children around him and told the people how important children were. He told the disciples to let them come to him, because he knew that children belonged to God and that God loved them very much (see Mark 10:13–16).

Grandma got out a pencil and paper. She thought of a way to show Shea that God is a loving Father-Mother right there in school to help her. Grandma wrote this poem for Shea and gave it to her mom. It includes three synonyms for God.

My Father-Mother LOVE
protects me
as I work and play.

My Father-Mother MIND
helps me understand
my lessons for the day.

My Father-Mother TRUTH
puts goodness in my heart
and brings good friends my way.

Thank you, Father-Mother GOD,
for being here with me,
and everyone,
in my school today.

Shea's mom loves God very much, too. She knew these words were true. The next morning, before the school bus arrived, she and Shea took some quiet moments. She read this poem to Shea. "Was that written for me?" Shea asked. And deep in her heart she heard its meaning.

When the school bus brought her home that afternoon, she ran up the driveway with a huge smile. She'd done her lessons well that day and had a good time in school.

Since then Shea has brought home many 100's and *A*'s. She's happy with her school and lessons. She has lots of friends and plays on the T-ball team.

Kate's grandma teaches a class in Sunday School. She asks the boys and girls to find page 582 in the book *Science and Health with Key to the Scriptures*. Then they read aloud that God's children are "representatives of Life, Truth, and Love." Isn't that great to know, wherever you are?

—Helen Elizabeth Williamson

Originally published in the September 13, 1999, issue of the *Christian Science Sentinel*.

It's True!

God made me happy, well, and strong—

Nothing about me can be wrong.

His perfect child I'll always be—

This truth is true for you and me.

—*Dorothy F. London*

Originally published in the December 6, 1999, issue of the *Christian Science Sentinel*.

Under Pressure? Pray!

They'd been told they would need a miracle to win even one victory. But here were Abby and her teammates, on the last day of the select invitational soccer tournament, in double overtime against the top-seeded team.

It had all come down to a shootout. Five players from each team lined up to take their turns shooting the ball at the net. Abby waited for her turn. She would be the last girl to kick. Her other teammates were yelling and shouting at each shot and miss.

Abby realized that to be able to kick at all, she needed to quiet her thoughts. But she knew that she didn't have to leave the field or shush people before she could get quiet. She'd found out that even in the middle of all the noise and excitement, she could get quiet if she prayed.

First, she thought about a verse in a poem that always made her feel peaceful. The words are from a poem by Mary Baker Eddy, called "Mother's Evening Prayer":

O gentle presence, peace and joy and power;
    O Life divine, that owns each waiting hour,
Thou Love that guards the nestling's faltering flight!
    Keep Thou my child on upward wing tonight.
        (*Christian Science Hymnal*, No. 207)

Abby was so busy praying that she didn't feel tense.

Her next prayer was one of her favorites, a simple one called "Daily Prayer": " 'Thy kingdom come;' let the reign of divine Truth, Life, and Love be established in me, and rule out of me all sin; and may Thy Word enrich the affections of all mankind, and govern them!' (*Manual of The Mother Church,* by Mary Baker Eddy, p. 41).

As she stepped up to kick, Abby felt calm. She kicked the ball right into the top left corner of the net. Her friends and teammates broke out into cheering and screaming. They raced onto the field, shouting and hugging each other. It wasn't until then that she realized she'd broken a tie to win the game. Abby said later she never thought about the whole game depending on her kick. She was just praying to reflect God.

Later the same week Abby prayed in this new way that she had learned at the game to help her study for final exams. Each time she started feeling afraid or overwhelmed, she thought about what had happened on the soccer field. There, when she'd been under a lot of pressure, she'd quieted her thoughts by praying. She could do the same thing when she had to take a grammar or math exam. And she did!

—Sara Hoagland Hunter

Originally published in the September 17, 2001, issue of the *Christian Science Sentinel.*

"Did that thought come from God?"

Lexi was just about the happiest little girl around. She loved everything—going to Sunday School, selling Girl Scout cookies, and especially playing with her new stuffed animal Tigger, the fun-loving character from *Winnie the Pooh*. Most of all, she loved her family so much that she would shower them with hugs and kisses throughout the day.

One night while Lexi was waiting for her mother to tuck her in, she had a very sad thought that made her feel afraid. When her mother came to her room, Lexi wrapped her arms tightly around her and said, "I never want to have to leave you. I don't want you to ever go away."

Lexi's mother knew right away that the thought that was making Lexi sad wasn't from God. She reminded Lexi about the "important question." Lexi had been learning to ask a very important question regarding thoughts. This question is, "Did that thought come from God?" *Science and Health with Key to the Scriptures* asks the question this way: "Are thoughts divine or human? That is the important question" (p. 462).

A divine thought comes directly from our Father-Mother God. The Bible tells us that God says, "I know the thoughts that I think toward you, saith the Lord, thoughts of peace, and not of evil, to give you an expected end" (Jeremiah 29:11). We always feel more loved, more safe, more comforted, when we know that God is speaking to us and when we remember to listen for His thoughts.

But what about the thought that made Lexi sad? These kinds of thoughts are called error because they are untrue and not from God. These wrong thoughts ask you to believe

something that isn't true about God or about you, His child. The thought telling Lexi that she could be separated from someone she loved was an error-thought.

Lexi's mother held her very close and told her: "God is Love, and you can never be separated from God's love. God never stops loving you, and He never takes away His love. Whatever God has given you to love will be yours forever." This made both Lexi and her mother feel safe, comforted, and very happy.

With that, Lexi rolled over to go to sleep. She rolled right onto Tigger, which made her giggle! She then began talking about everything she had to do tomorrow—painting the new sign for her clubhouse, selling more cookies, and doing all sorts of other fun things. She had completely forgotten the sad thought. It disappeared—and so had the sad feeling.

—Jean Wright Piper

Originally published in the April 13, 1998, issue of the *Christian Science Sentinel*.

A Little Boy and His Goliath

Mark went to the Christian Science Sunday School. Each week the teacher discussed Bible stories with the class. Then they talked about how to apply these stories at home or in school.

Mark had a brand-new bicycle he was very proud of. One day while he was out riding his shiny new bike, two bullies called out to him very unexpectedly. They told him they were going to take away his bike. Although Mark was very afraid, he said sternly, "No, you are not!" Then the boys began trying to grab the handlebars and shouted, "We *are* going to take your bike." Suddenly Mark remembered a recent Sunday School session on the story of David and Goliath (see I Samuel, chap. 17). He stood straight up and shouted at the bullies, "In the name of the Lord, you are not!" Puzzled, they pulled back. One said to the other, "He's a kook," then took off with his friend.

Though Mark was trembling through and through, he returned home still holding his bike and told his mother what had happened. Mark's face was pale, but she could tell he was stronger from having put down error.

Through Sunday School, Mark had been learning to face challenges with Truth instead of backing away from them in fear. He knew that the same power of God, good, that helped David stand up to Goliath could help him with any tough situation. He had learned that the giant Goliath stood for the lie that error, or evil, can be big and powerful when it isn't even real at all. He had learned that with trust in the truth of God's all-power, he could face up to any error, tiny or huge; whether it called itself sickness, fear, trouble in school, or some other kind of discord. He had learned that error is just a bluff, and that's what gave him the courage to stop the bullies trying to take away his bike.

"Evil is destroyed by the sense of good," writes Mrs. Eddy in *Science and Health with Key to the Scriptures* (p. 311). That "sense of good" can be with you just as it was with Mark. It will stop anything trying to take away the happiness and peace that belong to you as God's child.

—*Gladys C. Girard*

Originally published in the November 17, 1987, issue of the *Christian Science Sentinel*.

Today

Dear Lord,
keep me gentle,
kind.

Let my thoughts
be pure as
Thine.

— Dorothy F. London

Originally published in the February 25, 1980, issue of the *Christian Science Sentinel*.

Keep Singing!

Sometimes people think it isn't honest to say everything is all right when everything looks all wrong. They think you are only trying to fool yourself into believing it, just to keep the trouble from hurting too much, or to keep somebody else from finding out how bad things really are. But if God made all creation, as the Bible plainly says, it is honest to say that everything He made is good, and to believe it, too. God doesn't send evil to His children to cause them suffering. Where would He get evil in a good creation?

It is only error, or wrong thinking, which makes us believe that real things are bad or bad things are real. Very often, error seems to spread itself all around everywhere and then scream: "Look at me! Doesn't it frighten you to see the way I act?" Then if you say, "Yes," error often begins to look still worse and to frighten you even more.

Christian Science teaches us how to see right through those lies of evil by trusting God so fully that we cannot be made to believe anything ugly about Him or His children. Christian Science teaches us how to keep on singing and thanking God, and really mean it. Being happy and thankful brings many blessings. Here is a story of how happy singing once blessed a certain little bird.

Cheerio was a canary who lived in a cage with his mate in the sunroom of a beautiful home where there were two children. One evening the father of the two children came home from his office very, very weary. Nothing had gone right, and he felt as though there were a heavy brick on his heart. At the door the children met him with unhappy voices: "Cheerio is lost! We can't find him anywhere. He was flying around in the house, but he has not come back to his cage. We have looked and looked all day in every room."

So the father joined the search for Cheerio, happy little Cheerio, who always flew anywhere he wanted to in the house, perching here and there and singing his heart out joyously!

By bedtime they still had not found him, and it was not a very happy family that finally turned out the lights. In the morning when the children were dressing, suddenly they heard a bird's song. Cheerio! It was Cheerio's sweet morning song! Eagerly they all began the search again, trying to follow his song, which sounded small and far away. It seemed to be coming from the kitchen, but they hunted there carefully and could not find him. Then someone opened a kitchen drawer—and what do you think? Out flew Cheerio! He had a long piece of string in his bill, and he flew straight to the sunroom, where he and his mate were building a nest in their cage.

Cheerio had spied the string and darted into the drawer to get it, but before he could fly out, somebody had shut the drawer, not realizing he was in there. So all day and all night Cheerio had stayed in the dark, stuffy drawer, waiting for it to be opened. Maybe it seemed like a long time to him, and a very dark place; but suppose he had forgotten to sing. Perhaps no one would have found him. It was his song that freed him. Cheerio was waiting, with the string in his bill, for that drawer to be opened, and when it was opened, he wasted not a single second in going about his happy task again, still singing.

Do you know what the father said when they found Cheerio? He said if a little bird could sing in that black place, he could sing too, even though matters looked pretty miserable for him right at that moment. And he did.

Singing saved the little bird as easily as it would save a person, because gratitude is spiritual. It belongs to God, and whatever belongs to God belongs to Life, for God is Life. Thankfulness does not need words to make it shine. It needs a happy heart, and Cheerio's heart was happy.

Oftentimes people get so busy denying error that they seem to forget all about God's presence and think only of the error. When you work out an arithmetic problem, you don't say: "Two and two are not five, so I won't use five. They are not six, either, so I won't use six." Think how you could go on for hours, denying thousands of wrong answers, when all the time you really need only the one correct answer, which you could put down in the wink of an eye.

Our dear Leader, Mary Baker Eddy, says in her book, *Science and Health with Key to the Scriptures*, on page 412, "Mentally insist that harmony is the fact, and that sickness is a temporal dream." To "insist" means not to let up one second. "Temporal" is the word for something that lasts only a while, like a dream. If sickness were anything more than a dream, there would be nothing you or anyone else could do to make it go away. You can never wake up from what you really know, because your real Mind is the Mind which is God. But sickness and trouble and fear and sorrow are not Mind at all, and so you can awaken out of them. God will wake you up when you seem to fall asleep in error. He watches you always. He will not let any of His precious children drop from His sight, even though sometimes they seem to wander away by themselves and not want to be near Him.

When Jesus' work in this world was nearly finished, and he knew that he would not be with his disciples much longer, he said to them comfortingly, "Ye now therefore have sorrow: but I will see you again, and your heart shall rejoice, and your joy no man taketh from you" (John 16:22).

Jesus did return to his disciples for a few weeks after he overcame the belief of death, but he did something more wonderful than that. For all people everywhere, through all the years to come, he left the truth he taught and lived, and little children can use it. He left his joy with us, too, the sort of joy no one can take away. It really is true, that no one can take your joy from you. If it seems to go, you yourself are the one who has given it up. No one can take it.

The next time unhappiness knocks at the door of your thoughts, remember Cheerio, whose song was stronger than the darkness because God gave him his song. God has given you a song of joy too. Keep on singing it!

—*Jean Elsie Sanders*

Originally published in the July 22, 1944, issue of the *Christian Science Sentinel*.

What Elizabeth Learned From the Earthquake!

An earthquake is when the earth's crust moves or shakes. When an earthquake happened where Elizabeth lives, she felt afraid. Her mommy and daddy held her very close and comforted her. They told her how much they loved her. They also told her always to remember that she is safe in God's love.

Elizabeth was almost ready to start Sunday School, where she would learn about God as Love. Elizabeth would soon be able to look up all by herself the Bible verse that reads in part, "...God is love" (I John 4:8).

There is another book that is read in the Christian Science Sunday School along with the Holy Bible. It is *Science and Health with Key to the Scriptures.* A very kind and good woman named Mary Baker Eddy wrote the book. It helps people understand an important message of the Bible—that not only is God Love itself but God's love is all good and all around us.

The week after the earthquake, Grandma came to visit and baby-sit Elizabeth while her mommy and daddy had an evening out together. Elizabeth was especially happy because Grandma was spending the night. They always had so much fun together. They made wonderful things with the big blocks. They played grocery store. They went to the park and played on the swings. They took a walk and skipped, too. What Elizabeth liked the most was their pretend tea party.

After Elizabeth had gone to bed and Grandma was downstairs reading, there was another small earthquake, called an aftershock. The house shook so much that Elizabeth woke up. She cried out for Grandma. As fast as could be, Buck the dog raced up the stairs to Elizabeth's room with Grandma right behind him.

Elizabeth and Grandma hugged and hugged. Grandma wiped her tears. And Buck lay down on the floor by the bed.

"Grandma," Elizabeth asked, "are you afraid?" "No, little darling," Grandma replied (Grandma always called her "little darling" at special times).

Elizabeth was puzzled. "Why not, Grandma?"

Grandma pointed to Buck. "Is Buck afraid?" "No!" said Elizabeth. "How can you tell that he is not afraid?" Grandma asked. Elizabeth looked at Buck—"He's wagging his tail."—"That's right!" said Grandma. "Buck *feels* loved and safe."

Then Grandma asked Elizabeth to look at Roxie, her kitty, who was curled up on her bed. "Is Roxie afraid?" Just then, as Elizabeth gently touched her head, Roxie began to purr. "Roxie isn't afraid either because she *feels* loved and safe," said Grandma.

Then Grandma explained to Elizabeth that Grandma also feels love, and this love keeps her from feeling afraid. The Love that makes Buck wag his tail, makes Roxie purr, and makes Grandma feel unafraid *is God*. God made us and all that's good in our world with love, and this love keeps us safe.

"Do you know what another name for God is …?" Before Grandma could even finish her question, Elizabeth interrupted. She knew the answer.

"Love," she said with a grin. Grandma said, "Yes, little darling, and God's love is all around us. And when we remember this, we are not afraid."

Elizabeth, with tears all gone, snuggled back under the covers. She wasn't afraid anymore. She looked up and said, "Oh, Grandma, you are so special."

Grandma, filled with so much love, said, "Who told you that, Elizabeth?"

Smiling even more brightly, she answered, "Love did!"

Then Grandma asked, "How do you know that God is with you?"

Elizabeth's eyes got wider. "How, Grandma?"

"It's because you are here. Wherever you are, God, Love, is there! When we remember this, we can feel strong, brave, and safe. We feel unafraid."

Buck was not afraid; Roxie was not afraid; Grandma was not afraid; and now Elizabeth was not afraid either. Elizabeth and Grandma felt the power of Love around them all!

— *LaMeice Harding*

Originally published in the October 14, 1996, issue of the *Christian Science Sentinel.*

The Case of the Missing Ring

Jenni was excited about spending the night away from home. She packed her own suitcase, carefully folding her pajamas, playclothes, and warm sweater. She got her toothbrush and slippers. And she told her floppy bear stuffed animal that this was going to be a really fun weekend.

When everything was ready, Jenni stopped to slip on her special ring. It was shiny gold and had a small brown stone on top. Jenni loved this ring. It was not worth a lot of money, but it had belonged to her grandmother. When Jenni looked at it, it reminded her how much she loved her grandma and the happy times they'd had together. She smiled as she picked up her little suitcase, hugged her floppy bear, and headed out the door.

The weekend was filled with lots of activities. Jenni played outside, visited friends, ate at her favorite restaurant, and even stayed up past her bedtime. But when it was time to get ready to go home, all the fun memories seemed to disappear like a sandcastle in a heavy rain. Her ring was gone!

Jenni tried to remember everywhere she had been. She thought she had been careful not to wear the ring when she was playing outside, but she looked all around the bushes, the sidewalk, and the yard just the same. It was starting to get dark, and Jenni was getting more and more worried. Where could it be? She looked everywhere in the house, under chairs and beds, and in every corner. The missing ring was nowhere to be found. She began to cry and to feel sad that Mother had given her this precious ring of Grandma's.

But then an idea came to her: "I can ask God!" Jenni had been learning in Christian Science Sunday School about God's love for her. She knew many Bible stories about people who had a problem or were afraid and looked to God to help them. Like Moses and Christ Jesus. They trusted God to show them how to see His goodness everywhere. They proved through their lives and their healing works that no one can be separated from God. No one is alone.

Every night Jenni and her sister said a prayer together. It's a verse by Mary Baker Eddy for little children:

> Father-Mother God,
>   Loving me,—
> Guard me when I sleep;
> Guide my little feet
>   Up to Thee.
>   (*Poems*, p. 69)

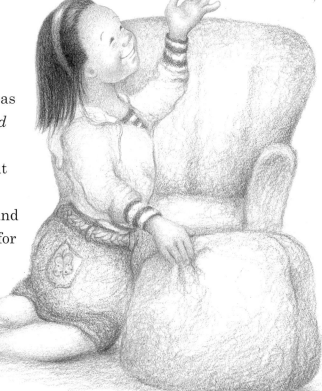

God answers our prayers by giving us ideas to guide our way. Jenni didn't ask God to *find* her ring. God doesn't know about lost rings, because nothing is lost to Him. Nothing is out of place in His creation. God is all good and governs His kingdom with harmony, order, and peace. Jenni knew that if she turned to God for help, she could trust in His direction.

Jenni also knew that she had to be willing to listen for God's answer. She decided to be very still and ask God to tell her what she needed to know. She filled her thought with God's love and care for her. It didn't matter that she was away from home. He was the Father of all, and He was in charge.

Very soon the idea came to look behind a chair cushion in another room. She had looked there several times already without success, so she didn't move. But the same idea kept coming, so Jenni decided to try once more. And there it was! Stuck deep behind the cushion was the sparkle of her gold ring. Jenni thanked God for always being with her and for showing her this proof of His care. It really had been a great weekend!

—*Ann B. Hymes*

Originally published in the April 10, 2000, issue of the *Christian Science Sentinel*.

Poor God? No Way!

It was Saturday morning. Andy was still in bed. Jodie was curled up on the couch reading a book when Mom called her.

Jodie was surprised to hear Mom say, "Andy isn't feeling very well this morning. He doesn't want to get up. I've been praying with him, but I have to get ready for work now. Maybe you could go in and talk to him. I'm praying, too."

Jodie knew that when Mom asked her to talk to Andy, Mom wanted her to help him remember some of the things he was learning about God and man in the Christian Science Sunday School. Jodie said "OK," but she wasn't sure what she was going to say to him.

Sitting on the edge of her little brother's bed, Jodie thought for a minute. She remembered how quickly each of them had been healed of mumps, and how Andy's foot had been quickly healed when a brick fell on it. There were other healings, too. Jodie said to herself, "Thank you, God" for all His care and love for them.

Andy had just started going to Sunday School, and he already knew a lot about God. He knew that God is Love, and that God is good. In Sunday School, he also was learning that God is perfect, and that man is His perfect reflection. Being God's reflection means being the likeness of God, Spirit. He knew that God's reflection has only what comes from God. God, good, can't be sick or imperfect, so His reflection, man, can't be sick or imperfect either. As God's reflection, Andy had to be perfect—just like God.

Andy was lying on his tummy with his head buried under the pillow. He knew Jodie was there, but he didn't say anything.

Suddenly, it came to Jodie just what to say: "Poor God!"

Andy lifted the pillow and looked at his sister.

She said again, "Poor God!" and added, "He must be feeling just awful today. I guess He's not going to be helping us or taking care of us, because He's just too sick."

Andy turned over and looked at his sister in disbelief. "No!" he said. "God's not sick. He can't be. He's perfect."

"Then you can't be sick either," said Jodie. "You're God's reflection, and you can only be the likeness of Him. So if you're sick, God must be, too."

Andy could see that he wasn't getting anywhere. How could he make her understand? Maybe he needed to talk louder to make her understand. "No way!" Andy shouted. "Mrs. Johnson, my Sunday School teacher, said God is Spirit. It says so in the Bible. That's why He's perfect." God is not material, so He can't be sick. He knows only good, and He doesn't know about sickness. He never made sickness.

"Are you God's reflection?" Jodie asked.

"Yes!" shouted Andy.

"Well, if God's not sick, then how can you be sick?" asked Jodie.

"I'm not!" shouted Andy.

"Then why are you staying in bed?" Jodie asked, starting to laugh.

"I'm not!" shouted Andy, laughing too as he threw back the blankets.

Mom came into the bedroom to check on all the noise just as Andy was climbing out of bed. He looked at her and said, "God's not sick today, and I'm not either." Mom gave him a big hug and reminded him about what Christ Jesus said: "Be ye therefore perfect, even as your Father which is in heaven is perfect" (Matthew 5:48).

Andy said, "God's perfect, so He's never sick. He loves me so much that He made me perfect just like Him." With that, Andy got dressed, and they all went downstairs for breakfast.

Andy was all better. After breakfast, he went to find his best buddy who lived next door. The two boys had a great time playing trucks in the sandbox.

—*Joan T. Lucht*

Originally published in the July 31, 1995, issue of the *Christian Science Sentinel*.

The Whale in the Pail

A long time ago there was a funny vaudeville act that made people roar with laughter. Vaudeville was a kind of show people had before television. You had to go to a theater to see it.

The star of this particular act was a hypnotist—a man who could put people who consented under a kind of spell. While it lasted, he could make them believe anything he told them.

First, he called for a volunteer from the audience, and when someone came up on the stage, he put him under his spell. Then he seated the person, handed him a fishing pole, and put a pail in front of him, telling him to cast his hook into the pail. Next, he cried out that a whale had swallowed the hook! And he ordered the man to land the whale.

The poor volunteer, believing that he really had caught a whale in the pail, naturally struggled and groaned and perspired, trying to pull such a huge creature out of so small a container.

The people watching this silly exhibition generally laughed so hard at the fisherman that they gasped for breath! When the hypnotist snapped his fingers and the volunteer wakened to what was really happening, you can just imagine how foolish he felt. How could there ever be a whale in a pail!

Maybe you too are laughing at this absurd act. But aren't we sometimes just as foolish as the fisherman, and don't realize it? Sometimes we let mortal mind fool us into thinking we have a problem. We think we have to work hard to get rid of the problem—just as the man was working hard to pull the whale out of the pail, when there wasn't any whale there in the first place!

Oh, yes, you say, but you *do* have a problem! You think your friend is angry at you or you hurt your knee.

The man thought he had a whale, too. He needed to work, not to pull a whale out but to wake up from the hypnotism that made him believe something that was not true. And we need to work in Christian Science, not to change our friend or our body but to see the truth of our friend and our body. Then we are free, made free by the truth as Christ Jesus said we would be.

In the first chapter of Genesis we are told that all things God made—the earth, the heavens, the stars, the sun and moon, man, all living things—are God's spiritual reflections. God, Spirit, sees everything He makes as very good.

God doesn't make a man with problems. God makes man perfect, and "whatsoever God doeth, it shall be for ever: nothing can be put to it, nor any thing taken from it" (Ecclesiastes 3:14).

So if God doesn't make mistakes, sadness, pain, or anger, where do such problems come from?

They come from where the whale in the pail came from—nowhere!

And where are they? Just where the whale that seemed so very real was—nowhere!

We can't put into God's universe something He didn't make! Where could we get it, since God made everything that was made?

Mrs. Eddy writes, "Impossibilities never occur" (*Science and Health with Key to the Scriptures*, p. 245). She also says, "There is but one creator and one creation" (p. 502).

Good is all. This means that the problems we seem to have are not real; they are false beliefs. There just isn't any place for them in God's harmonious universe. God is Love. Everything He makes has to be loving and good. Love surely couldn't make anything to harm or frighten us.

Then how do we get rid of the problems we think we have?

How did the man "get rid" of the whale? He simply woke up! And that's what you need to do.

If God made everything harmonious, and if He is the only creator, it is impossible for us to have a real problem. Right?

So okay, we can stop struggling to pull an old whale out of a pail.

We'll just wake up to God's presence, His love for us, and His everlasting goodness. We'll know that God and man are perfect, and right where the problem seemed to be we'll find that all is well.

We can laugh at error's silly performances.

We're not going to believe something that isn't true.

We're Christian Scientists. We're awake!

—*R. Louise Emery*

Originally published in the August 8, 1970, issue of the *Christian Science Sentinel*.

Tommy's Proof

"Did you strap the bikes on the car, Tommy?" Mother shouted from inside the house.

"Yep, and the beach bags are in the trunk. Hurry up, Mom, so we can have a ride around the lake before lunch."

Tommy was in a hurry to get to Green Lake Park. He loved riding his bike along the shady paths, and he liked the smell of hot dogs cooking at the roadside stand where they ate their lunch. He was hoping the sun would warm the lake enough so they could swim in the afternoon and then go beachcombing.

At last Mom was in the car, and they were on their way to pick up Sally and Jane—Mrs. Cashon's granddaughters. Mrs. Cashon, Tommy's friend and Sunday School teacher, was in front of the house with the girls and their beach bags when Tommy and his mother pulled up. The girls were eager to get to the park too.

Tommy was out of the car by the time his mother turned off the motor. He flipped the front seat forward so the girls could get in, and then he went around to talk with Mrs. Cashon, who was watching his mother rearrange things in the trunk.

While describing the trails by the lake to Mrs. Cashon, Tommy traced a map with his finger along the groove where the trunk lid closes. Not knowing the finger was there, his mother closed the lid and put the car keys into her huge pocketbook.

Tommy's finger was wedged. He couldn't move. He was so scared he couldn't even yell. Then he felt Mrs. Cashon's hand close over his. Their eyes met and he knew she must be praying, so he wasn't quite as scared. Realizing what had happened, Tommy's mother started digging in her purse for the keys to the trunk.

Mrs. Cashon, who was a Christian Science practitioner, spoke softly to Tommy. "You know that God loves you, don't you, Tommy?"

"Yesss," Tommy's voice quivered.

"You know you are God's beloved child."

Another "Yesss." This time Tommy felt surer.

"As the child of God you are His likeness, and since God is Spirit and cannot be smashed, you can't be hurt either."

His mother found the keys and the lid opened. Tommy was free, but the finger didn't look too good. "Look to God and His goodness, Tommy, not at the finger," Mrs. Cashon said as he got into the car.

It was hard to hold back the tears, but Tommy tried, and he waved at Mrs. Cashon as they drove away.

A couple of times during the ride the finger hurt, but instead of looking at it, Tommy thought about God and His goodness. He had learned in the Christian Science Sunday School that, as Mrs. Eddy says, "God is everywhere, and nothing apart from Him is present or has power," (*Science and Health with Key to the Scriptures*, p. 473). Soon the pain stopped. Tommy and Jane and Sally went off riding their bikes, swim-ming in the lake, eating hot dogs, and combing the

beach for agates. It turned out to be a wonderful day, and it was over much too soon.

That night when Tommy was showing his dad the agates he had found and telling about the good time they'd had, he didn't even mention the hurt finger. He'd forgotten about it. Next day when he did look at the finger, it had only a thin red line that didn't even hurt and that soon disappeared. But Tommy remembered the quick healing for a long time. It was his proof that it's a good thing to look to God.

Note to parents:

Tommy's mother was greatly concerned for her son's welfare. Since trust in God had always brought healing for her and her child, she was confident that the practitioner's immediate attention and prayer would be effective in this situation.

Mrs. Cashon spoke to Tommy in words she knew he would understand. Children who study Christian Science learn very early that God is Love, all-powerful, and everywhere. In a recent Sunday School class Tommy had learned that God created man in His image and likeness (see Genesis 1:26). The class had also talked about what Christ Jesus accomplished—healings of disease, accident, blindness—through looking to God, good, as the only power. Jesus said, "Verily, verily, I say unto you, The Son can do nothing of himself, but what he seeth the Father do: for what things soever he doeth, these also doeth the Son likewise" (John 5:19).

Both Tommy and his mother knew that Mrs. Cashon was giving Christian Science treatment (applying the law of God's present power to the situation). Such prayer was far more than asking God to heal a smashed finger. It was an affirmation that man's true identity is not material but spiritual, for it is in God, Spirit, and therefore intact. The results were in accord with Mrs. Eddy's statement, "The prayer that reforms the sinner and heals the sick is an absolute faith that all things are possible to God,—a spiritual understanding of Him, an unselfed love" (*Science and Health,* p. 1).

—Thelma J. Shipman

Originally published in the March 1, 1982, issue of the *Christian Science Sentinel.*

Change the Slide

While Dad plugged the slide projector into the wall socket, Ricky bounded up and down on the sofa. He could hardly wait to see the slides of summer camp he had taken all by himself. Dad switched the light off, and there was the camp swimming pool on the screen. Ricky told what happened in each slide. Mom and Dad laughed at the weird costume Ricky had made out of an inner tube and an old apron.

With the slide show finished, Dad switched the light on. "How about showing these slides to Grandpa and Grandma when they come Saturday?"

"Great!" Ricky said.

But Friday afternoon when he got home from school Ricky didn't feel well. Mom went into his room to find out what was wrong. "I guess it's flu. Everyone at school is talking about it," he said and sighed. "I wanted so much to show Grandpa and Grandma the slides tomorrow night." He hid his face in his pillow.

Mom sat down beside him. "Remember how your Sunday School teacher talked about holding in thought what you really are—the spiritual child of God, made in His image?"

Ricky nodded. "But I don't feel like God's child right now."

Mom smiled. "That's because you're looking at the wrong slide."

"The wrong slide?"

"You're looking at the picture of a miserable boy, not the joyful, spiritual child God knows you to be." Mom picked up Ricky's *Science and Health with Key to the Scriptures*.

"Mrs. Eddy says, 'You embrace your body in your thought, and you should delineate upon it thoughts of health, not of sickness' (p. 208)."

"What does 'delineate' mean?" Ricky asked.

"It means to draw or picture something. Now, your thought is something like a slide, and what your thought pictures about your body is what you'll see. Ricky, if you want to change the picture on the projector screen, do you go to the screen and try to rub it out?"

"No. I change the slide. I get it. Thinking about having the flu is like putting in one slide, and thinking of God's perfect child is like putting in another slide."

"That's it. And you can always decide for yourself which slide you want to look at," Mom said. She handed Ricky *Science and Health*. "Now look up 'the scientific statement of being.'"

Ricky had been memorizing it for Sunday School; he turned to page 468, but he didn't even have to read it. " 'There is no life, truth, intelligence, nor substance in matter,' " he said by heart.

"Do we think this belief of flu has any intelligence or substance?" Mom asked. "Do we want to accept it as true of God's child?"

"No."

"Then, let's reject it the way we'd toss out a camp slide that wasn't any good. What's the next sentence?"

Ricky read, " 'All is infinite Mind and its infinite manifestation, for God is All-in-all.' "

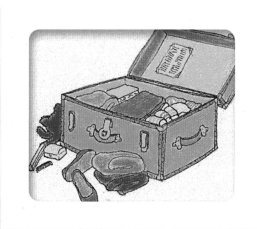

Mom smiled. "OK, as God's spiritual, perfect child, you can only be touched by what

God sees and knows. You can only have health and joy and goodness—all Godlike qualities—because nothing else can exist, since He is All. That's the slide you want to keep in the projector."

They went over the rest of "the scientific statement of being." By the time they got to "Therefore man is not material; he is spiritual," Ricky looked up. "Know what, Mom? I don't feel hot anymore. I'm OK!" Mom gave him a hug.

The next evening Ricky showed his camp slides to Grandpa and Grandma. They laughed at the funny inner tube costume. Ricky was glad they liked his camp and the slide show. But he was even happier that he had learned something about changing slides—he could always look at the picture of God's spiritual, perfect child.

— *Keo Felker Lazarus*

Originally published in the September 27, 1982, issue of the *Christian Science Sentinel*.

Never Alone

God is where I'm going,
God is where I am.
He is here beside me
and He holds me by my hand.

God's love is on my school bus,
His love is in the park.
And if it rains or thunders,
or gets very, very dark,

the truth of God is with me
and with everyone I know.
Like sun reflecting sunbeams
God is everywhere we go.

He knows what we are doing,
and He shows us where to stand;
God always is beside us
and He keeps us in His hand.

God is where I'm going,
God is where I am.
He is here beside me
and He holds me by my hand.

—Kerry M. Knobelsdorff

Originally published in the January 12, 1987, issue of the *Christian Science Sentinel*.

Being Just Me

Did you know that each kind of bird has its own song? A robin sings a robin song, a cardinal sings a cardinal song, and a bluebird sings a bluebird song. Each song is different. If you know the different songs, you don't have to see the bird to know what kind of bird it is. You can tell just by hearing his song. There is a "trick" bird, though—the mockingbird. This bird learns many different sounds and birdsongs and combines them all!

You are made to have your own "song." By that I mean there's just one you. No one else, not even a twin or a very close brother or sister, could ever be you. You were made by God to be special—to have special talents and to love in your own special way. No one can ever take your place. No one can ever be *you,* and you can never be anyone else. God needs you to be your own special self! And He gives you all you need to do that perfectly well.

Sometimes we get tricked into thinking we're not as special as someone else or that being ourselves is not good enough. We might even start acting like that tricky mockingbird, copying other kids who we might mistakenly think are better than we are. We might try talking, dressing, or acting like them. But no matter how hard we try, we can *never be* them and they can never be us. In fact, if we could change places with them, we wouldn't be happy at all because we're made to be only us.

What if you're not happy with who you are? The only way this could happen is by not *knowing* who you really are! To get and stay happy with yourself you must know yourself. How? By asking God to tell you who you are. God knows you better than anyone else does, better than your mom or dad, your best friend, or even yourself! God knows everything about who you really are because He made you. You are His child.

Jesus heard an important message from God. It was this: "This is my beloved Son, in whom I am well pleased" (Matthew 3:17). Jesus taught us that we are all the sons and daughters of God. So, God is just as pleased and happy with us! He *loves* us! And He's *satisfied* with the way He made us in His image.

That's nice to know, isn't it? God is satisfied with us, so *we* should be satisfied with ourselves, too. Satisfied *now*. Not when we get older, taller, wiser, or faster. Not just when we win an Olympic gold medal or get straight *A*'s in school.

I have a sister who's only one and a half years older than I am. When we were younger, I thought she was a queen! She could always do more than I could, better than I could, sooner than I could. She was funnier than I was, and it seemed as if everyone, including me, liked her more.

I often tried to copy her, but that didn't make me any happier or make others like me any better. Looking back, I see copying her really just kept me from finding my own special talents and using them. I finally had to start getting to know "me." I had to listen to God to find out what He wanted me to do and say and be. As I listened and obeyed, I discovered some special talents I didn't even know I had. And what I found was fun and satisfying!

I saw that I was actually pretty different from my sister *and* that it was OK. We weren't better or worse than each other, just different. Kind of like two pieces in a puzzle, each very different but each needed to make the whole picture.

We need to go straight to God and follow what He tells us. Jesus never copied other people just to be like them. When he was about 12 years old, he went to the synagogue and listened to and questioned the scholars and lawyers. For him, learning didn't come from copying other boys or even the scholars and lawyers but from listening directly to God and obeying Him. By doing this so carefully and completely, he was also able to heal. He taught the people about God, and we are still learning from Jesus' example today. He did all that by being the "self" he got from God.

As we learn to listen to and obey God, we'll find out more and more about our "specialness." We'll get better and better at what we're supposed to be doing, what we're made to do—express God, good. And we'll be so happy and satisfied being our real selves and doing good things.

By following faithfully what God tells us to do, we will shine brightly and help others see that they can do the same. What a fun variety we'll see! What "songs" we'll all have to share, whether we share them as musicians, writers, mountain climbers, runners, cheerleaders, basketball players, mechanics, or computer geniuses. We'll just *be* what God would have us be—and we'll just love being it.

—*Joan Sieber Ware*

Originally published in the May 19, 1997, issue of the *Christian Science Sentinel*.

Testimony

It had rained earlier that morning. All the fourth graders were out at recess. I was walking with one of my friends. We came to a slide and I jumped up on the end of it. As I jumped onto the slide, my feet went out from under me and my stomach hit the slide very hard, taking my breath away.

My friend helped me up and walked me to a teacher. She sent me to the nurse's office. The nurse asked me what had happened and how I felt. I told her about the accident and said I felt faint and hot. My mom happened to be working at the school that day, so the nurse went and found her.

I wanted to go home. The nurse agreed that was a good idea, and she suggested that we might want to call a Christian Science practitioner because she knew that's what we would want.

When my mom and I got home, I read articles in the *Sentinel* and prayed. Because my stomach still hurt I called a practitioner to pray with me. I thought about what I had learned in the Christian Science Sunday School about God creating everything and making everything good. As I was thinking about these things, I decided I would like to work with a Concordance to *Science and Health*.

Here is one sentence I found: "Under divine Providence there can be no accidents, since there is no room for imperfection in perfection" (p. 424).

I knew that if accidents are not known to God, there can't possibly be anything to hurt me in God's kingdom.

The next day I didn't go to school. I stayed with my mom and dad at home. We read the Bible Lesson from the *Christian Science Quarterly* together and worked with some more ideas that the practitioner had given me, in addition to the statement and Bible verses I had already found on my own. I still was having trouble walking and standing upright, but I was making progress. We all kept praying.

The next day I was able to go back to school—walking fine and feeling good, too. Boy was I happy!

I am very grateful for my healing. I am glad that I was able to pray for myself and be healed.

— Courtney Moore

I am very happy to verify our son's testimony. When the school nurse came to get me, she was calm and reassuring, but she had observed that he was very uncomfortable and light-headed. When I got to her office, Courtney and I began to pray quietly together and to talk about the fact that God was right there with us.

It was very natural for the nurse to suggest that we would probably want to call a Christian Science practitioner. Five years before, when Courtney first started attending this school, the nurse visited with me to talk about how my husband and I rely on prayer for the care of our children. During those five years, our family has formed a wonderful friendship with this nurse, and she has always been supportive of our family and of our religion. When Courtney returned to school feeling fine, she rejoiced in his healing with us.

I was very grateful to see Courtney wanted to call a practitioner to talk to him and pray with him, and to see Courtney study specific citations in the Bible and *Science and Health*.

Isaiah said, "A little child shall lead them" (Isaiah 11:6). I feel this child and his childlike trust led us past the fear to see evidence of God's love, care, and healing presence.

— Nancy Lynn Moore

Courtney has experienced many wonderful healings over the years. In this instance it was gratifying to see him take his own initiative in praying and applying what he has learned in Sunday School about his harmonious, perfect relationship to God.

Through this occasion and others with our son, we have had the opportunity to share Christian Science with the nurse at his school. As a result of her desire to learn more about spiritual healing, the nurse has attended a Christian Science lecture, obtained a copy of *Science and Health*, and taken a role in supporting efforts to preserve religious freedoms through our state legislature.

I am most grateful for the many tangible ways in which Christian Science has blessed our family and others with whom we have had the opportunity to share it.

— *Miles Montgomery Moore*

In verifying Courtney's testimony, it is important to stress the potentially serious nature of his injury. After the incident, he came to the office with great difficulty, bent in pain, and extremely pale. I had very strong concerns.

Under virtually any other circumstance I would have referred the student to a physician's care. However, knowing the Moore family and the extent of their faith, it was very natural and comfortable for me to release Courtney into the hands of his parents and their practitioner. Within a day and a half he was back in school, completely well.

Reflecting on the situation has been very encouraging to me, for it reinforces what I have come increasingly to realize in knowing the Moores—the powerful, strengthening, healing effects of faithful prayer. Theirs is a growth-producing testimony which enriches all who are privileged to observe it, but especially to me in my own personal spiritual realm, as well as the professional setting. I am renewed.

— *Ruth Graves, school nurse*

Originally published in the March 16, 1992, issue of the *Christian Science Sentinel*.

God Never Made a Bully

Michael was in the fourth grade and had always enjoyed going to school. He liked his teacher and got along well with his classmates. He and his mom would often talk together about his day, and he liked to share with her what was going on in school.

But then he started telling his mom before school that he didn't feel like going that day. On some days, the school would call her at work to tell her to come and get him from the nurse's office. Yet by the time they got home, Michael would be feeling fine.

Michael usually told his mom everything that happened at school, but now he seemed unable to tell her what was troubling him. Whenever Michael's mom knew he was facing a problem, she would pray for him, so she prayed now. Even though she didn't know exactly what the problem was, she knew there were no secrets from God. She decided to schedule a conference with Michael's teacher.

At the conference, Michael's teacher helped Michael tell his mom about Curtis, an older boy who had a history of harassing younger students. He was in Michael's reading group of fourth-, fifth-, and sixth-graders, and this year he had chosen Michael as his target. He would trip him in the classroom, push him into his locker, and sometimes take his school supplies. The teacher said that talking with Curtis's family wouldn't help, since he was treated harshly by his father. Previous talks with the family hadn't changed anything.

When they got home from the conference, Michael and his mom decided to pray together. They talked about seeing Curtis as the image and likeness of God, his true

Father, who loved him. They also reviewed seven words from Mary Baker Eddy's definition of *God* in *Science and Health with Key to the Scriptures*: "Principle; Mind; Soul; Spirit; Life; Truth; Love" (p. 587). They reasoned that if God is Mind and God is Love, He could impart only good and kind thoughts to all His children. They also found these two powerful promises in that same book: "Love must triumph over hate" (p. 43), and "Clad in the panoply of Love, human hatred cannot reach you" (p. 571).

Michael and his mom promised each other that they would love Curtis unconditionally, just as God did. They refused to see any child of God as being a bully. Now Michael had a plan of action—to see as true only what God knew about Curtis. He knew that he could always trust God to keep both Curtis and himself safe and happy.

Michael put these thoughts into practice at school. He wasn't afraid of Curtis anymore. He could even be friendly toward him! In a few days, Michael began to smile in the morning and once again looked forward to going to school. Curtis had stopped acting like a bully, and they even became friends!

When Michael's mom had her next school conference, the teacher not only told her what a good job Michael was doing, but also commented on the remarkable change for the better in Curtis's behavior. They were both grateful for the end of the problem.

—*Joy V. Heinlein*

Originally published in the September 14, 1998, issue of the *Christian Science Sentinel*.

Peter and the Bees

It was a beautiful, sunny day, and the children could not wait to change out of their school uniforms and into their swimsuits.

They ate lunch and did their homework in record time. "Last one in is a frog!" yelled the eldest child, Peter, and there was a mad dash as his younger brother and two sisters raced outside to make sure they would not be last into the pool.

Suddenly, in the middle of all the laughter, Peter screamed. On the grass around the pool were hundreds of blossoms that had fallen, and among these blossoms were many bees searching for nectar. Peter had been stung when he stepped on one of the bees.

Immediately, his foot began swelling, and he cried in pain. His mom rushed to see what had happened, and carefully helped remove the stinger. At the same time, she comforted Peter by reminding him of some of the spiritual truths he had been learning in Sunday School. There, his class had talked about how much God loved them and how He was taking care of them right now. His mom realized that she and Peter needed to get a clearer understanding of these truths, because he had been stung frequently that summer. And she knew that God would never want His beloved child to be hurt.

They went inside and began reading from a book that Peter had been getting to know, along with the Bible, in Sunday School. This book is called *Science and Health with Key to the Scriptures* and was written by a woman named Mary Baker Eddy. They read this sentence: "Understanding the control which Love held over all, Daniel felt safe in the lions' den, and Paul proved the viper to be harmless" (p. 514). They talked about the fact that if God, who is Love, is in control of all His creation, then nothing that He created is ever out of His control. If Daniel had not been eaten by the lions and Paul had not been harmed by

a snake, how could Peter have been harmed by a little bee?

They read further on the same page, "All of God's creatures, moving in the harmony of Science, are harmless, useful, indestructible" The little bee was certainly useful and had been going about its business collecting nectar for the whole hive. It had never meant to hurt Peter, just as he had never meant to hurt it. Peter saw, therefore, that he could not be angry with the little bee, but had to love and forgive it.

He and his mom read in the Bible that when God created the earth, He gave man dominion—authority—over "the fish of the sea, and over the fowl of the air, and over the cattle, and over all the earth, and over every creeping thing that creepeth upon the earth" (Genesis 1:26). So it was clear to Peter that a bee's sting could not have authority over him and cause him pain because, as God's child, he had dominion over all. As he began to understand these wonderful truths, the pain stopped.

Peter soon ran out and joined the others. It was not long before the swelling of his foot went down, and he was able to wear his normal shoes to school the next day. In the past when Peter had been stung, this had not been possible until days later. Even more wonderful was the fact that never again was he stung by a bee in that garden. He and his family continued to live in the same house for a number of years, the blossoms continued to fall on the grass, and the bees continued to buzz busily among them. But because Peter had seen so clearly that Love is always in control and that "all of God's creatures ... are harmless, useful, indestructible," the bees didn't harm him.

Over the years, his family has used these same truths to overcome the effects of hornet and sea urchin stings. More recently, his mom was healed of a severe dog bite. What a blessing Peter's experience turned out to be!

—*Brenda May Dry*

Originally published in the May 1, 2000, issue of the *Christian Science Sentinel*.

"Thou shalt not steal"

Alan had saved his own money to buy special handlebars and a special seat for his bike. He had worked hard to install these all by himself and was proud to show his mother what he had done.

One evening Alan forgot to put his bike in the garage; and the next morning it was missing. He ran to his mother crying, "Someone has stolen my bike!"

His mother told him that now was the time to put into practice and to prove the truths he had been learning in Sunday School from Jesus' Sermon on the Mount and also the commandment God gave to all men, "Thou shalt not steal" (Exodus 20:15).

She read these words to him from *Science and Health with Key to the Scriptures* by Mrs. Eddy: "The thief believes that he gains something by stealing, and the hypocrite that he is hiding himself. The Science of Mind corrects such mistakes, for Truth demonstrates the falsity of error" (p. 294). Then Alan's mother said that he might begin to see how he could correct his thinking with the truths Christian Science teaches about the commandment, "Thou shalt not steal."

Alan searched the commandment to see how it applied to him. He knew that God, Truth, made man in His likeness, and therefore God's idea, man, is truthful. Since man is Godlike, he cannot steal, for God cannot steal. Since the only real man is the man made in God's likeness and since God is everywhere, there can truly be no one anywhere who steals. And since there is no thief to steal, Alan knew that there was no one who wanted to steal from him.

Then he saw that if he believed that someone had stolen his bike, he was violating the ninth commandment, "Thou shalt not bear false witness against thy neighbour" (Exodus 20:16).

For he was really bearing false witness when he was believing that God's idea could do something the Father-Mother God had never made man able to do.

Alan started earnestly to try to obey both of these commandments. Each time he thought about his bike being gone, he would apply the truths learned from these commandments.

In a few days a schoolmate told Alan that he thought he had seen his bike while delivering papers in another part of town. That afternoon Alan and his mother went to the location and got the bike. After a few adjustments were made, the bike was as good as ever. Alan was happy to jump on and ride again. But he had also learned something very important. He had proved for himself that the commandment, "Thou shalt not steal," also means thou shalt not be stolen from.

—Marjorie Ponder Matchette

Originally published in the February 12, 1966, issue of the *Christian Science Sentinel*.

Sally and the Ball

Ⅰt was a bright and sunny morning, but Wendy was very sad. She didn't feel like getting up. She didn't feel like going out to play with her friend, Richard. She didn't feel like doing much of anything.

When she finally went downstairs, Daddy could see that something was wrong. So he asked what was the matter. At first, Wendy didn't want to tell him. But finally she said, "I wish I had a shiny new tricycle like Richard's. Mine is all old and scratched up, and it's got dents all over it."

Daddy's answer surprised Wendy. He didn't talk about tricycles at all. Instead he asked Wendy if she'd ever heard the story of "Sally and the ball." Wendy said, "No. What's the story about?" So Daddy told her this story:

"Once upon a time there was a little girl named Sally. One day her mommy came home from the store with a present for her. It was a shiny little red ball. Sally was very excited and happy. She thanked her mom. Then she ran outside to play with her new ball.

"But soon Sally came back into the house crying. She said one of her friends had a bigger and much nicer ball than hers, and she wanted one like that. So the next day, her mommy went to the store and bought Sally a new ball, just like the one her friend had.

"Again Sally thanked her mom, and with a big smile on her face she ran outside to play with her new ball. But it wasn't long before she came home again in tears. Guess what! Someone else had an even bigger and nicer ball than Sally's, and she just had to have one like that.

"So the next day her mommy went to the store and bought Sally another new ball just like the one her other friend had. Sally was so happy. Again she thanked her mom and went out to play with her new ball."

Then Daddy asked Wendy if she could guess what happened next. Wendy said that Sally probably came in crying because someone else had an even bigger and nicer ball.

Daddy told Wendy she was exactly right. Then he asked if she thought this story would ever end. Wendy thought about that for a few moments, and she said, "I guess it probably won't."

Then Daddy pointed out that no matter how many material things we have, such as balls or tricycles, we can always find someone who has something that is bigger or better. "So, if we think that in order to be happy, we always need material things as big as or better than someone else's, we're going to spend a lot of our time being sad," Daddy said.

Then Wendy remembered something she had learned in her class in the Christian Science Sunday School. It was one of the Ten Commandments: "Thou shalt not covet..." (Exodus 20:17).

Coveting means wanting what someone else has, her teacher had said. People who covet don't understand that really we already have all the things that are good and that make us happy, because they all come from God. These are not material things like tricycles and balls. They're spiritual qualities such as intelligence, joy, and love. God, who is Life, Truth, and Love, gives them to His children every minute of every day.

Wendy and Daddy talked about this a little bit. Then she thanked him for telling her such a good story and ran outside to play. As she climbed on her tricycle, there was a big smile on her face.

—Beverly Wallace Lydiard

Originally published in the June 6, 1983, issue of the *Christian Science Sentinel*.

The Reflection In the Still Pool

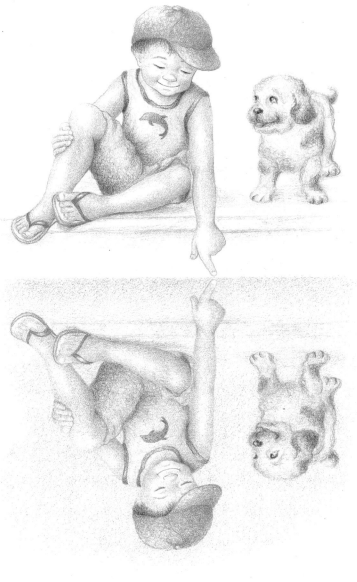

For Matt, one of the special joys of winter is the swimming pool! A hotel near his house lets neighbors come and use its indoor pool. There can be a bitter cold wind howling outside, but inside the pool area, it's always steamy hot.

One day when Matt arrived, the pool area was empty except for the lifeguard. It was so quiet. There were no voices or splashing sounds echoing off the windows. The water was completely still. Matt's mom gently stopped him at the edge of the pool. She asked him to look at the water and tell her if he noticed anything.

"The water looks just like a mirror," Matt said. He also pointed out, with a laugh, how many chairs, tables, and umbrellas had been added to the room. What he saw in the water was a reflection. There had always been tables, chairs, and big, open umbrellas all along the edge of the pool. Now, because of the reflection in the pool, it looked like there were twice as many of them. Looking into the still pool, Matt's mom took just a moment to explain something about God and about man as His image and likeness.

"You're seeing a perfect reflection of what's near the pool because the water is so still,"

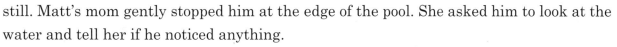

she said. "Matt, you know how sometimes the water is all stirred up? Even then, the reflection is still there, only you might not see it very clearly.

"Each of us is really the spiritual reflection of God. That's a fact! When we are still inside—when we listen for God's thoughts and feel His love—we can see God's nature reflected in ourselves and others. We can see it expressed in qualities such as love, honesty, and intelligence.

"God is always good, and so is His reflection. Sometimes, though, we're just not alert to that good. But when our thoughts are still and loving, we can feel and see His good nature expressed all around us."

Matt's mom also told him about a sentence found in the book of Psalms. It says, "Be still, and know that I am God" (46:10). With that, the two of them jumped into the pool and had a great time playing.

That evening Matt's mom showed him several sentences in *Science and Health with Key to the Scriptures* by Mary Baker Eddy that talk about man as God's reflection. He especially liked the sentence, "Man is, and forever has been, God's reflection" (p. 471).

A few days later Matt was outside, chasing around with friends. While he was looking behind him, he ran full speed into a parked car. His mom came right to him when she heard his cry. At first he didn't hear her say anything because he was crying so loudly. Then he realized she was talking very quietly to him. He could hear her whispering softly in his ear—"Be still." He wanted to look at his hand because his thumb hurt a lot, but it was gently closed in his mom's hands. Instead, he heard her whispering, "Remember the still pool. Be still and know and *feel* that God—only good—is perfectly reflected here."

Matt became very still inside. He thought about the quiet pool and how the reflection of the tables and chairs and umbrellas had been perfectly clear. The reflection was not distorted in any way. The details of the original were exactly the same in the reflection.

Matt had learned in the Christian Science Sunday School the teaching of Christ Jesus that God is Spirit and that He is perfect. So Matt knew that as God's reflection he must be spiritual and perfect. He could express only God's qualities, such as freedom and joy. Suddenly, he also remembered the word *forever* from the sentence Mom had read from *Science and Health*. There is no starting and stopping in *forever*. Nothing can separate God and His reflection, man, for an instant; therefore he couldn't be touched by an accident.

Right now and always, God is forever reflecting Himself perfect and unchanged.

Praying this way didn't take long. Matt looked down and saw that his hand was fine. Isn't it comforting to know that we all reflect Almighty God? This is truly an awesome fact—it's worth remembering!

—*Stephanie S. Johnson*

Originally published in the April 17, 1995, issue of the *Christian Science Sentinel*.

Here and There
And Everywhere

When you're going out and coming in
God and His love are there with you.
He's at the place that you just left,
And already at the place you're going to.

He's right now, right there, where you are;
He is ever-present Truth.
You can't get away from Him if you try.

WHO WOULD EVER WANT TO?!

—*Nina Rose Jackstadt*

Originally published in the February 26, 1996, issue of the *Christian Science Sentinel*.

I Feel Free!

When I was growing up, there were lots of times when I didn't feel free. Sometimes I felt sad and lonely. Sometimes I felt confused or discouraged. At those times, I would go down to the basement and sit on the big sofa. My dog, Betsy, would always come and sit with me. She comforted me. She also taught me a lot about freedom.

Betsy *lived* freedom. When she was a puppy, we made a small fenced area in the basement to keep her in one spot. She always found a way out. When she got bigger, we gave her half of the basement. But she learned to jump up on the door and turn the doorknob with her paws!

Finally, my dad built a tall fence around the backyard. That would keep Betsy in for sure! She sat in the backyard watching Dad work very hard. Then, just as he finished nailing in the very last board of the gate, she gave a little run, sailed through the air, and went right over that gate! Nothing could keep Betsy from being free.

We each have a God-given right to be free. We're free to follow God by listening to and obeying Him. We're free to be happy, healthy, and whole. We have a right to be free from every sad, lonely, or sick thought. We read in *Science and Health with Key to the Scriptures*: "God made man free. … Citizens of the world, accept the 'glorious

liberty of the children of God,' and be free! This is your divine right" (p. 227).

Does freedom mean we can do whatever we want? No, real freedom never means that we can break the rules. Real freedom comes only through exact obedience to rules, to God's law, God's will, God's way. Through obedience we can find complete freedom now, even if it seems as though we're caged by sadness, limitation, wrong behavior, or sickness.

First, we need to understand that God is All and that He is completely free from any limitation, fear, sickness, or lack. Since this is true about God, that's all that He can express in man—in you, me, and everyone. We are made to express all the good that God is. God needs each one of us in order to fully express His goodness and love.

Once we understand that God is all good and that we are one with Him, we know to obey His goodness moment by moment. We must do what God wants us to do, think what God wants us to think, be what God wants us to be. It's knowing the truth about God's goodness and living as an expression of good that make us free. Jesus told his disciples, "Ye shall know the truth, and the truth shall make you free" (John 8:32).

Knowing and living God's goodness help us know the difference between the good we should do and the mistakes we should avoid. If something is not good, then it's not from God and is no part of you, His child. You can't even want it or wish for it. God tells us all, "If it's not like Me, then it's *not* you. If you can find it in Me, then you can find it in you!"

When I was a kid, I proved that knowing the truth about God and man makes us free. I had trouble with earaches. Sometimes my mother or a Christian Science practitioner would pray with me. Sometimes I prayed by myself. The earache would always stop, but I was still afraid of getting one again, especially if I went swimming underwater. Finally, I began to understand that I had a right to be free—free from the earaches, free from the fear, and free to swim. Earaches aren't good, so they couldn't be from God. Since they're not from God and they're not like God, they were never really mine, either. God makes all of us free, happy, and whole, and He keeps us that way always. As I began to understand God better, I began to feel less afraid and more free. The trouble with my ears ended once and for all. Now I especially love to swim underwater, feeling just as free and natural as a porpoise!

Knowing what's true about God and you means freedom. Being free is always possible because freedom is a part of living in God's kingdom.

—*Joan Sieber Ware*

Originally published in the December 7, 1998, issue of the *Christian Science Sentinel*.

To Be a Good Soccer Player…

I love to play soccer. God helps me get goals because He gives me all my abilities. In Sunday School I made a list of the things my soccer coach told us we need in order to be good soccer players. Then I added the spiritual ideas that help me do this.

My coach's list:

Know who to pass the ball to and how to pass the ball. · · · · · · · · · · · · · ·

Keep your head up to see what is going on. ·

Protect yourself. ·

Keep the ball in front of you to have control. · · · · · · · · · · · · · · · · · · ·

Acknowledge your teammates. · · · · · · · · · ·

Be a good sport. ·

Be fast. ·

Practice. ·

Stay in position. ·

Stay positive. ·

My list:

▶ Trust in God to know what to do.

▶ God keeps you alert and aware. He is All.

▶ You're always in God's kingdom, so you don't need to be afraid that you'll get hurt.

▶ Keep God in front of your thought. God is in control.

▶ Be nice to those around you. You can do that because God made you that way.

▶ Have fun. You have joy from God. God creates it. You express it.

▶ Run with God along the way.

▶ Use what you've learned about God. Pray and DO IT.

▶ Be obedient to God. Your helpers are the Ten Commandments and the Beatitudes.

▶ Always think good thoughts. Listen to God.

I hope you like these ideas. They helped me, and I hope they help you, too!

—*Andrew Soley*

Originally published in the October 15, 2007, issue of the *Christian Science Sentinel*.

The Five G's

Joe needed help, and he felt that he was all alone. It was not that there were no other people around him, but none of them were students of Christian Science.

Joe had started attending the Christian Science Sunday School when he was three years old. On his very first Sunday he had learned that God, good, guides, guards, and governs His children always. His mother called these words the five G's and helped him to remember that God was caring for him every minute of every day. Joe often repeated these words, especially when error tried to whisper that everything was not as it should be.

Now Joe was spending a few days in the mountains with a friend. The two boys had a fine time hiking in the mountains, rowing on the lake, and sitting by the campfire at suppertime. When night came, they were both ready to go to bed after such busy days. Joe always went right to sleep, but one night he awakened later and found that his head was hot and his throat was sore and dry.

Up to this time, whenever Joe needed help he would ask his mother what to do and she would tell him what to read from the Bible and from *Science and Health with Key to the Scriptures* by Mary Baker Eddy. She had also helped him by knowing the truth of man's perfection as God's image. But now Joe's mother was in the city, sixty miles away.

As he lay there trying to think of something he had learned in Sunday School that would help him, Joe suddenly remembered the five G's which he had learned so long ago. "God, good, guides, guards, and governs me," he thought. Then he reasoned that because God is good, He knows nothing about error. He never made error; and if God didn't make it, nobody did. Therefore it isn't real.

Joe was becoming interested in this line of thought, and he began to think about the word *guide*, which means to "show the way." For instance, an airplane coming in for a landing is guided by the person in the control tower so that it will fly on the safest course. God, too, guides His children. Suddenly Joe remembered reading in *Science and Health*, "Whatever guides thought spiritually benefits mind and body" (p. 149), and he knew that at that very moment God was guiding his thinking.

Joe then went on to the next word, *guard*, which means to "protect." He knew that God protects His children, and that He was protecting him right then by giving him these good thoughts. Error cannot get in when one's thinking is good.

Governs was the next word, and as Joe thought of it he was glad he had paid attention in Sunday School, because just the week before, his teacher had talked about government. Part of the Golden Text from the Lesson-Sermon in the *Christian Science Quarterly* had read, "...the government shall be upon his shoulder" (Isaiah 9:6). And in the first section of the Lesson this statement had been found: "Divine Love corrects and governs man"

(*Science and Health*, p. 6). Joe knew that to understand that God governs man through divine Love could only bring about healing in his experience. He remembered some other words of Mrs. Eddy's, which can be found on page 393 of *Science and Health*. They read, "Man is never sick, for Mind is not sick and matter cannot be."

"I know this is the truth," thought Joe, and with that he fell asleep. The next thing he knew, the sun was shining brightly and the smell of bacon was drifting up from the campfire.

Joe arose and dressed quickly, for he was well and happy. No one in the camp knew that he had been awake a long time in the night. And as he went down to breakfast, he was grateful for the Christian Science Sunday School, where he had learned that God, good, guides, guards, and governs.

—Grace B. Millings

Originally published in the February 16, 1952, issue of the *Christian Science Sentinel*.

Bursting Balloons

To burst most balloons, all you need is a sharp pin. One good prick and—*bang!*—all that's left is a shriveled piece of rubber.

The balloon may have only just been blown up, or it may have been around awhile. It may have been quite small or fairly large. It doesn't matter to the pin, nor to the person holding the pin. Can you imagine standing in front of a helium balloon—even one that's quite large and that has lasted a week—with a small, very sharp pin in your hand and saying, "I don't know if this pin will burst that balloon; it's so old and so big"?

Well, every word of Truth can be like a sharp pin to error[1] we may see blown up around us like balloons. Fear or hurts may seem big, they may even seem old; but spiritual truths can burst them quickly. The Bible says, "The word of God is quick, and powerful, and sharper than any two-edged sword" (Hebrews 4:12).

How can we be sure of this? The life of Christ Jesus has examples. For instance, one night Jesus and his disciples were in a boat on the Sea of Galilee. While Jesus slept, a storm began. Frightened, the disciples woke Jesus. He knew God cares for His creation, and so he said, "Peace, be still" (Mark 4:39) to the wind and waves. And they were calm. The disciples were pretty impressed by this. Jesus spoke the truth, the word of God.

Mrs. Eddy says, "Speak the truth to every form of error" (*Science and Health with Key to the Scriptures*, p. 418). When anything tries to make us feel that bad people or sickness might be around to hurt us or make us unhappy, we can say, "No, you don't, because God is the only power. And that is the truth."

Then watch the *error* let go. We'll see that it was just a lot of air—nothing at all!

—*Carolyn M. Hook*

[1] Mrs. Eddy uses the word *error* to talk about evil, or things that are material and untrue.

Originally published in the April 22, 1985, issue of the *Christian Science Sentinel*.

The Armor of Good Thoughts

Saturday was here at last. Jeff had invited his friend Rick over for the afternoon. At first they played in the tree house in the old apricot tree in the backyard. After a while they decided to climb to the top of the tree and slide down the rope ladder. Just as Jeff reached the ladder, he stepped on a weak branch and came tumbling to the ground, scraping his back on a rough bough.

Rick came quickly to Jeff's aid. Both boys were students in the Christian Science Sunday School, so it was natural for them to use the truths they had learned of God and man.

As Rick helped Jeff into the house, he reminded his friend of the place in the Bible where it says, "God is our refuge and strength, a very present help in trouble" (Psalms 46:1). Rick said: "God does not cause accidents or know about them, for God knows only harmony. You live in God, good; so you can never be in pain."

While Mother put a bandage on Jeff's back, she told both boys that this was an opportunity to learn more of God's protection. She reminded them that Christian Scientists follow the teachings of Christ Jesus by turning to God, divine Love, to direct them at all times. They trust their ever-present Father-Mother God to protect His children.

Jeff got his Bible and read what the Apostle Paul wrote about trusting God. This is what he read: "Stand therefore, having your loins girt about with truth, and having on the breastplate of righteousness; ... . And take the helmet of salvation, and the sword of the Spirit, which is the word of God: ..." (Ephesians 6:14, 17).

Mother then asked the boys if they could explain what Paul meant. Jeff answered: "The breastplate of righteousness is right thinking about ourselves and others. It's knowing we are really spiritual ideas of God, pure and free, reflecting Him."

Then Rick spoke up and said: "The helmet of salvation means that when we try to understand more of God, we are safe in the arms of Love, wherever we may be. The sword of the Spirit is the word of Truth, which destroys fearful thoughts."

Jeff knew that a Christian Scientist is always alert in his thinking. He opened *Science and Health with Key to the Scriptures* by Mrs. Eddy and read: "Stand porter at the door of thought. Admitting only such conclusions as you wish realized in bodily results, you will control yourself harmoniously" (p. 392).

Very soon Jeff felt well enough to go back to play. As he and Rick walked back to the tree house, they remembered Mrs. Eddy's words, "Good thoughts are an impervious armor; clad therewith you are completely shielded from the attacks of error of every sort" (*The First Church of Christ, Scientist, and Miscellany*, p. 210).

Jeff and Rick played the rest of the day. Jeff was grateful for his healing, but most of all for a better understanding of how to be a Christian Scientist.

—Jacqueline Fisk Sayre

Originally published in the November 12, 1966, issue of the *Christian Science Sentinel*.

The Mirror and the Rainbow

Do you have a favorite mirror in your house? One you use to check to see if your hat is on straight or your socks are matching? No matter whether you're going to school or spending a Saturday playing in the woods with your friends, you want to let the best "you" show.

What do you see when you look in the mirror? Do you see a boy or girl? Straight hair or curls? Any freckles? What do your friends and family see? How do you see those around you? These are good questions to ask yourself. But the most important question is, "How does God see me and everyone?"

When we look in a mirror, we see only the outside covering. We may see a bright orange dress or a faded pair of jeans and sneakers. But that's not who we really are. We're so much more.

The very first chapter of the Bible, called Genesis, says that God made all of us in His image and likeness. Now, if you are the image of God, that means you reflect God. Mary Baker Eddy writes in *Science and Health with Key to the Scriptures*, "As the reflection of yourself appears in the mirror, so you, being spiritual, are the reflection of God" (p. 516). And since God is good, you express that good. What else is God? He is

Love, so you are loving. He is Spirit, so you are spiritual. He is Truth, so you are honest.

Each of us is made up of qualities such as joy, goodness, peace. These qualities are the real you and me, the real Mom and Dad, the real Lesley and Darryl and Sara and Robert. They're like the colors of the rainbow. If you had to pick one color from the rainbow—or one quality of God—that reminds you of yourself, what would you choose?

Now think about this: because you reflect God and God is All, you really express *all* of God's qualities. It's like expressing all the colors of the rainbow.

How can you start to see the full "rainbow" of qualities that's you? Well, what if you made a list of all the good qualities that you reflect as God's child? And what if you taped that list to your mirror? Then every time you looked in the mirror, instead of seeing just one color, you'd think about the whole rainbow of qualities that you express. And what if you started to see your friends and family in all of their glorious colors? Then you would be seeing yourself and others the way God does. And what a big, bright, beautiful view that would be!

—*Whitney Woodruff Moody*

Originally published in the March 1, 1999, issue of the *Christian Science Sentinel*.

Unzip the Rabbit!

Soon after Charlotte started going to school she was often ill, and it seemed a shame.

So her mother, who knew about Christian Science, asked a friend who was a Christian Science practitioner to come and see Charlotte.

The practitioner came. She brought with her a Bible, and *Science and Health with Key to the Scriptures* by Mrs. Eddy. She showed Charlotte the place in the Bible where it says, "So God created man in his own image, in the image of God created he him" (Genesis 1:27) and in *Science and Health* where it says: "Man is spiritual and perfect; and because he is spiritual and perfect, he must be so understood in Christian Science. Man is idea, the image, of Love; he is not physique" (p. 475).

"So you see, Charlotte," said the practitioner, "you are Love's perfect idea."

Charlotte had beautiful manners, but she was also puzzled, so she said politely: "Yes, I can see that *really* I am God's perfect child. Christ Jesus said that everyone is. But what about this *me* which is so often sick and can't go to school?" And she added, "There seem to be two kinds of *me.*"

"Do you like dressing up," asked the practitioner, "and pretending to be something or somebody else? Have you ever dressed up as a rabbit?"

Charlotte never had, and the practitioner explained that you can buy a furry suit like a rabbit, with long ears, and you put it on and zip it up, and there's a rabbit! (Charlotte thought that sounded rather fun.)

"Now," continued the practitioner, "I might see you lolloping down the street, and I might think: 'Gracious! there goes a very large rabbit!' But when you got home, would your mother think that?"

Charlotte laughed. "No, Mummy would unzip the rabbit, and find me."

"Then what would happen to the rabbit?"

"There never was a rabbit."

"But there was. I saw a very large rabbit lolloping down the street. And where were you, when I saw the rabbit?"

"Oh, dear," said Charlotte, "you really are mixed up. There was only ever me. There never was a rabbit; there was just *me* all the time. The rabbit was never real. Can't you *see?*"

"Yes," smiled the practitioner, "I can see. And I can see, too, that there's only one you now, the perfect you, Love's perfect child. Let's unzip the make-believe belief that you can be anything else."

And they did.

Charlotte was hardly ever ill after that. And if she was, she could usually see her own perfection by herself, or with Mother's help.

They would do this by understanding what is really true of man as God's beloved child, and by knowing that anything unhappy or sick is not real. *Science and Health* says, "If sin, sickness, and death were understood as nothingness, they would disappear" (p. 480). That's the way to get the better of any false belief.

—*Rosemary Cobham*

Originally published in the January 22, 1972, issue of the *Christian Science Sentinel*.

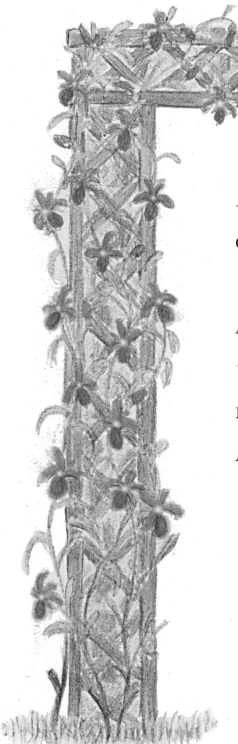

A Little Prayer

Our Father who art in heaven,

We thank Thee for Thy care,

And all the blessings Thou hast given

We would with others share.

May we Thy loving children be

And find our life and joy in Thee.

—W.

Originally published in the August 8, 1903, issue of the *Christian Science Sentinel.*

When Softwing Flew the Coop

Softwing is a cockatiel, a beautiful bird from Australia. He has gray and white feathers, a yellow plume on his head, and orange cheeks. He loves to sit on people's shoulders. He also likes cracked ice cubes, and he always says, "Hi, bird!"

One morning, while Addie, Softwing's owner, was at school, her mom opened the front door to get the mail. She forgot that Softwing was perched on her shoulder. Can you guess what happened? Off flew Softwing, straight up into the sky and out of sight.

Addie's mom felt very bad. She was upset with herself for being careless. And she was afraid that Softwing might not be able to find his way home. Softwing knew every corner *inside* their house, but he had never been *outside* of it before. Addie's mom decided to call a Christian Science practitioner to help her pray about Softwing.

The practitioner read this Bible verse to Addie's mom: "If I take the wings of the morning, and dwell in the uttermost parts of the sea; even there shall thy hand lead me, and thy right hand shall hold me" (Psalms 139:9, 10). Then she said, "Even if Softwing has flown far away, God is guiding him and holding him safe in His hand."

When Addie got home from school and found out that Softwing was missing, she called the practitioner, too. Addie told her, "I know God can keep Softwing safe. But how are we going to get him *back*?" The practitioner assured her, "There is always a way for good things to happen. God is the creator of Softwing and of you, Addie. He has made both of you entirely good and intelligent. That's what God knows about you two, and that's what's real about you both. God would never let part of His creation get lost or be unhappy or afraid. It's a divine law that everything God has made is always in its right place. You can prove that this law of God works."

Addie then prayed this prayer that she has loved since she was little:

> Father-Mother God,
>   Loving me,—
> Guard me when I sleep;
> Guide my little feet
>   Up to Thee.

> (Mary Baker Eddy, *Poems*, p. 69).

Then Addie prayed again:

> Father-Mother God,
>   Who loves Softwing,
> Guard him while he's gone;
> Guide his little wings
>   Back to me.

Another day went by, and Softwing still had not come home. Meanwhile, it rained and rained and got cold. Softwing had never been out in the rain and cold before. Addie and her mom had to pray really hard not to be afraid for Softwing. Addie's papa prayed with them, too. Then Papa decided to call the local newspaper and tell them that Softwing was missing.

Early the next morning, the phone rang. A man was calling from a town seven miles away. He said, "I was getting gas at a gas station, and I heard a bird singing. A little cockatiel was sitting on the ground near me. He hopped up on my shoulder and wouldn't leave, so I brought him home. I called the newspaper, and they gave me your name. Could it be your bird?"

Addie's mom was so excited. She said, "If you get some ice cubes out, we'll know in a minute if it's Softwing." The man's wife brought some ice, and the cockatiel flew over and landed on her shoulder. The bird said, "Hi, bird!" It was Softwing for sure!

Her family drove to the man's house, and they thanked him and his wife for taking care of Softwing. When her mom and dad picked up Addie from day care, she was so glad to see her bird! She thanked God for keeping Softwing safe and helping them find him. She couldn't wait to call the practitioner and tell her that Softwing was back. Addie was so glad to have proved that God, the creator, cares for all Her creation—children and cockatiels, too.

—*Maryl F. Walters*

Originally published in the January 15, 2001, issue of the *Christian Science Sentinel.*

Better Than Swimming in the River

Summer camp was far from my home and family! But I liked everything.

There were breakfast hikes with bacon and pancakes cooked outdoors by the river. There was roasting marshmallows in the campfire at night. We learned the funniest songs and made puppets and put on shows.

Best of all, the summer I was eleven I finally learned to swim. When I first arrived, I had to swim in the beginners' pool, a wooden pen with a board bottom. But by the end of my stay I had graduated to the river. I was able to swim halfway across the river where a landing was anchored.

It was all lots of fun, but I missed my family; sometimes at night I felt terribly lonely. Then, to make it much worse, one afternoon I slipped in the wet entrance of our shower cabin and tumbled down the stairs to the concrete floor below. The other girls and the counselors came running, asking, "Are you hurt?" "Do you want to go to the camp nurse?" My friends were worried. I felt alone since, as far as I knew, I was the only Christian Scientist there.

I said I would be all right and thanked everyone for wanting to help. I was barely able to stand up, and my back hurt. I couldn't walk without bending over. I was afraid, and then I really missed my parents and their love and support.

I took my Bible and *Science and Health with Key to the Scriptures* by Mrs. Eddy, to a quiet area under a shade tree.

I was so glad to have my books. They had always brought help when I read them, so I began reading the Bible Lesson[1] and I felt calmer. Then I thought of a Bible verse I had once memorized: "The eternal God is thy refuge, and underneath are the everlasting arms" (Deuteronomy 33:27).

This really helped me know for sure that God's arms had always been around me. God loved me and He never had let me go. He was all-knowing and He knew only good. No bad thing, no mistake or misstep, could touch the child of God. And an accident was a mistake, an error about what was possible in God's love. Then I thought of something I had learned in Sunday School: God, good, guards, guides, governs, loves, and lifts us up. My parents probably would have reminded me of all this. I was so grateful these good thoughts came to me even without someone else to talk with.

As I sat under the tree, I wasn't afraid anymore. I knew God was right there with me so I wasn't really alone. I was feeling the loving presence of my Father-Mother God. I just felt sure that Mrs. Eddy's words "Divine Love always has met and always will meet every human need" (*Science and Health*, p. 494) were completely true. And that meant God, Love, was meeting my need right that minute.

When it was time for dinner at the dining hall, I was walking a lot better. Later when I went to campfire, I walked normally and I wasn't even thinking about my fall. I overheard a couple of girls talking. "Say, isn't that the girl who fell down the stairs today?" one said. "I think it is. But she looks OK," the other said. That was the end of it for them—and for me.

I was glad not to get any more attention. I didn't want to be pitied or be treated like a special person. I only wanted to go on quietly trusting God, feeling His love.

It was just so good to be with my camp friends. We were like a huge family, and I could feel that love, the way I did back home with my own family. As I've said, learning to swim that summer was important. But finding that my Father-Mother God was always present and would heal me—that was the best!

—*Mary Lee S. O'Neal*

[1] The Christian Science Bible Lesson for each week is found in the *Christian Science Quarterly*.

Originally published in the June 27, 1988, issue of the *Christian Science Sentinel*.

Learning to Listen

The summer I was 12, my parents took all the family north to a remote lake in the Canadian woods. To me, there was nothing more fun than going for a tramp in the woods with my dad while on a fishing trip or camping out.

But this day, after lunch, without telling anyone, I decided to go for a walk alone into the dense brush. And what a walk it turned out to be! I tried to walk slowly and carefully, and I saw a fawn, a beaver pond and beavers, eight partridges, and a snowy owl that landed so close to me that I could count his tail feathers.

I was so excited seeing all this wildlife that I really wasn't paying attention to where I was going. Then, suddenly, I realized the day had become cloudy, it was getting late, and I had no idea where the lake and home were. I was lost.

For a moment I was afraid. But then I remembered how often Christ Jesus had shown people that they didn't need to be afraid (see Luke 12:32 and Luke 8:50). I knew that God is Love and is everywhere, and that I was His beloved child. My family went to the Christian Science church, and I had seen proofs of God's all-presence and all-power. Usually I had asked my dad or mom for help through prayer when I was afraid or needed something. But this time I was on my own.

I had learned in the Christian Science Sunday School that Truth, which is another name for God, is always with us and gives us the answers we need. So my next step should have been to listen totally to Truth, right?

Well, instead of turning to God first, I tried to think of any advice I'd ever heard about what you should do when you're lost. One person had said: "Look for moss because it will be growing on the side of the tree facing north, giving direction." Another had said: "Choose a clearing in the woods, get up on something high there like a rock, and wait for someone to rescue you."

These ideas didn't work for me. I found moss growing on *every* side of trees. And sitting on a high rock only made me aware of how hard the rock was. I went back to prayer.

But this time, instead of pleading with God, I thought about what I knew to be true about Him: that He is Spirit, ever present and All. He sustains all of His creation in Love, and that included me, His perfect likeness. I knew that with God loving and protecting me, I was safe right then. And with God leading the way, I would get safely home.

For a while it seemed like there was an argument going on in my thought about which direction to take. And I was afraid that if I didn't listen to the right thoughts, I would get more lost! But I remembered a story in the Bible about the prophet Elijah, who was alone in the wilderness in a frightening situation, and he heard God speak to him in "a still small voice" (see I Kings, chap. 19).

It must be true that God speaks to us in our thought and we can hear and trust Him, I reasoned. We can't be separated from God or get lost in His creation.

I remembered my Sunday School teacher reading a Bible passage one Sunday not long before. It was from Proverbs: "Trust in the Lord with all thine heart; and lean not unto thine own understanding. In all thy ways acknowledge him, and he shall direct thy paths" (3:5, 6). I started walking. I kept walking for what seemed a very long time. Then I saw through the woods ahead, against the darkening sky, a tall pine tree. It towered above all the rest. Near its top was a branch like a bent finger. I knew that branch. I knew that tree. I had seen it before from our log-cabin window. And I was soon back home.

I thought: "Thank God." And I did.

As it turns out, my parents had been praying, too. They said that when they prayed, they knew that God, who is Love, was my ever-present guardian. Our family had had a lot of healings and wonderful experiences of protection through prayer, and this was one more we wouldn't forget. Mary Baker Eddy, who founded the Christian Science Church, wrote a poem called "Feed My Sheep." I'd sung it as a hymn in Sunday School for as long as I could remember. But now it had a special meaning for me. Part of it says:

> I will listen for Thy voice,
>   Lest my footsteps stray;
> I will follow and rejoice
>   All the rugged way.

(*Christian Science Hymnal*, No. 304).

This experience meant a lot to me because I learned that even when I feel like I'm alone, I'm really never alone. God is with me and He is helping me. As I got older, there have been other times when I felt somewhat confused or "lost"—not in the woods but in some situation where I didn't know what to do. And I remembered what I learned: the moment you turn to God you are no longer afraid and you know you're not lost. Just trust God and listen. And you'll be led in just the right way.

—*J. Don Fulton*

Originally published in the March 16, 1992, issue of the *Christian Science Sentinel*.

All of Us Are the Children of God

What can you do when you are treated in a way that is unfair and mean? When Allison Gates faced a situation like that, she and her mom, Amy, decided that they could pray. And when they did, something quite special resulted! Here they are, telling about the experience that happened last year when Allison was in the third grade.

Allison: Well, one day I was riding bikes with my friend Ali, who lives up the street from me. We were riding on a street called "Hillside." And the boy who lives at the end of the street had lots and lots of friends over, and they were riding bikes, too. It was like a party.

The boys started teasing me for some reason. I was going to ride up the driveway, but one of them sort of jerked his handlebars and his wheel. Because he jerked so fast, it made my bike fall over. I fell down and really hurt myself. I scraped my knees. After that, he said, "Boy, was that a nice one. I should do that again sometime."

After that I just didn't know what to say.

Mrs. Gates: I can remember you came home and needed a lot of comforting. We washed off your knees and got you all cleaned up and helped you stop crying.

Allison: We prayed to know that all of us—including the boys—are spiritual children of God.

Mrs. Gates: We talked about God being Love and being our Father-Mother. And about how the great love of our one Father-Mother was not only embracing us but also loving those boys—instructing them, just as Love instructs us.

Allison: And we remembered a story from the Bible. It was about how Christ Jesus healed a man. When some people were taking Jesus away to be crucified, one of his disciples, Peter, didn't like that and knew it was unfair. He hurt one of the men badly. And Jesus knew that that wasn't the right way. So, Jesus just healed that man, even though those people were the ones who were taking him away to be crucified (see Luke 22:50, 51 and John 18:10, 11).

Mrs. Gates: We talked a lot about forgiveness, didn't we?

Allison: Well, at first it was really hard to find that feeling of forgiveness in me, but finally it just sort of came through and I was able to forgive.

Mrs. Gates: Allison, where do you think that feeling of forgiveness came from?

Allison: I think it came from God. I think that it was the power of God's love that really made me have the feeling of forgiveness for the boys. If Jesus could heal a man who was taking him to be crucified, I think I could forgive some boys that made me have a scrape on my knee.

Mrs. Gates: Even though the disciple, Peter, had done something that mirrored the roughness and unfairness of what the man was doing, Jesus wanted his disciples to know that that was not right. He wanted them to get the message that they must see themselves and others as God's likeness, not as mean or evil. They could trust God to correct, and they could trust God to govern and to heal.

Allison: When I do something not so good, sometimes my friend Eric does something to get back at me. I think that's sort of what the disciple did to the man.

Mrs. Gates: I think so. Mary Baker Eddy wrote a poem that she titled "Love," and it's in the *Christian Science Hymnal* as a hymn (No. 30). You sing it in Sunday School, and we sing it at home, too. The first verse says:

> Brood o'er us with Thy shelt'ring wing,
>   'Neath which our spirits blend
> Like brother birds, that soar and sing,
>   And on the same branch bend.
> The arrow that doth wound the dove
> Darts not from those who watch and love.

We wanted our prayer to shine forth with our Father-Mother's love. We didn't want any more arrows—harsh thoughts—darting around wounding anyone.

Allison: Right after that, we heard the doorbell. I ran to get it. I didn't know who it was, but I always love to get the door. So, I opened the door before my sister got there. And I saw the boys. There were so many of them, some of them had to go on the sidewalk. And I was so surprised. They said, "Allison, we hope you're OK and we're sorry."

Mrs. Gates: It was so different from the experience half an hour before with those same boys. We were deeply moved by this direct evidence of God's loving and embracing us all. We shared a few tears of joy and gratitude, didn't we? Later in that day I called the mom of the boy who'd had all the boys at his home. I asked her if she was aware that you'd been hurt and that the boys had come here. I wondered if the boys had told her what they had done and if she had made the boys come to our house to apologize. But when I spoke with her, she knew absolutely nothing about it. So they had done it on their own. It was so obvious that Love had led them to do it.

Allison: We were just so thankful to God for that experience. And my knees are all right, too!

—Amy Gates and Allison Gates

Originally published in the October 14, 1991, issue of the *Christian Science Sentinel*.

Debbie's Goal

Most people have goals. Some really work at them, some just dream about them. Maybe the latter figure they don't have a chance, so they don't want to try and fail. Or maybe they don't pick their goals wisely to begin with.

A friend of mine, named Debbie, had a goal that was really important to her. She wanted to be a cheerleader when she went to high school the next year. She started practicing months ahead. She learned how to lead all the school cheers, and she worked out on the trampoline.

And she prayed. Meaning, in her case, she asked God for His help. When school started and the cheerleader tryouts drew close, she prayed a lot harder.

But after the tryouts, she was miserable and talked with her Sunday School teacher. "Prayer doesn't work," she told her. "I prayed, and I practiced. I did everything I could. But they didn't choose me."

"Debbie," her teacher asked, "can't you trust God to supply what is best and happiest for you?"

Debbie looked a bit doubtful, so her teacher explained: "Instead of asking God to do us a favor or to give us some special thing we want, we need to be *willing*. We need to be willing to accept God's guidance, no matter where He leads us.

"It's good to aim for some worthwhile achievement, like being a cheerleader," her teacher added, "but in our prayers we still need to give up self-will and to pray as Christ Jesus did, '...not as I will, but as thou wilt' (Matthew 26:39). God's will brings good to us and to everyone, greater good than we can outline.

"Debbie, your prayers have not been wasted. Neither has all your hard work. And when you find your goal fulfilled, it isn't going to mean that someone else is done out of her goal."

She suggested that Debbie study the following sentence by Mrs. Eddy in *Science and Health with Key to the Scriptures:* "In the scientific relation of God to man, we find that whatever blesses one blesses all, as Jesus showed with the loaves and the fishes,—Spirit, not matter, being the source of supply" (p. 206).

We may think we have to compete with others for our goals, and that can lead to fear we will fail. The truth is that God has unlimited ways to bless us all, and as we are willing to love and trust Him, wonderful things happen. Sometimes in ways we could never have expected or even hoped for.

A hymn in the *Christian Science Hymnal* by Elizabeth C. Adams says it this way (No. 188):

> No eye hath seen, nor tongue declared,
>   Nor hath it entered heart of man,
> To know what God hath here prepared
>   For them that love and trust His plan.

My friend Debbie found this out. Shortly after she had failed to be chosen as a cheerleader, someone invited her to try out for a very special track team. She did, and won a place on the team. All her vigorous preparation for cheerleading turned out to be just what she needed for this new activity.

She had a wonderful year. The kids on the track team became very close friends. Besides that, they set some new records in their area.

As it happened, the next year Debbie did get chosen as a cheerleader and enjoyed that activity for the rest of high school. But now it didn't seem so important to her anymore. She had learned that God answers our prayers in wonderful ways. When we pray to Him and are willing to trust Him, the results are always good.

The Bible promises us, "…God is able to make all grace abound toward you; that ye, always having all sufficiency in all things, may abound to every good work" (II Corinthians 9:8).

—*Helen M. Leadbeater*

Originally published in the May 29, 1976, issue of the *Christian Science Sentinel*.

A Prayer

God is my friend and God is my All.

When I listen to Him I know I can't fall.

God's child can't be sick; I never have been.

I know that God loves me and I am His friend.

—*Celia Story*

Originally published in the October 17, 1983, issue of the *Christian Science Sentinel*.

Who Is My Best Friend?

Carolyn hurried into the house, hiding her face. She didn't want anyone to see that she was crying. Going to her room, she closed the door, lay down on her bed, and gave way to tears.

She had been riding her bicycle after dinner with her friend Denise and three other children who had just moved into the neighborhood. They had decided not to ride bicycles anymore but to go into the new neighbor's backyard and play tether ball instead.

While Carolyn was putting her bicycle away, Denise whispered to the three other friends something which Carolyn could not hear. When Carolyn joined them again, Denise told her that they did not want to play with her anymore, and the children ran off, leaving her alone.

Finally, Carolyn sat up on her bed, wiped her eyes, and thought, "A fine friend *she* is!"

Just then Mother opened the door to Carolyn's room.

"What's the matter, dear?" she asked, quick to notice that something was wrong. Then she added: "Why, you're crying. What is it?"

Carolyn sobbed. "It's Denise," she said. "She won't play with me. Neither will anyone else."

Mother sat down next to her on the bed and put an arm around her. "Well, now, I'm sure it will work out."

"No, it won't," Carolyn shook her head. "They're always doing it. Denise tells them to. And she's my best friend!"

Mother's face was serious. "Maybe it's time you stopped crying and started to do something about it," she said.

Carolyn dried her eyes and went to her bookcase. She took out a copy of the Concordance to *Science and Health with Key to the Scriptures* by Mrs. Eddy that had been given to her when Mother had bought a new one.

"I'm going to find out just what a friend is," Carolyn declared.

Mother smiled. "That's a good idea," she replied. "Maybe you'll find that Denise is not your *best* friend after all."

"If Denise isn't, who *is* my best friend?" asked Carolyn in surprise.

But Mother did not answer her question. "We'll talk about it later, dear," she said.

When Mother had left, Carolyn opened her Concordance. Mother had taught her how to use it, explaining that it is an alphabetical index of all the principal words in *Science and Health*. Carolyn found the words *friend* and *friends*. Below them were the page and sentence number where the words can be found. Carolyn went down the list, looking up each citation and reading it.

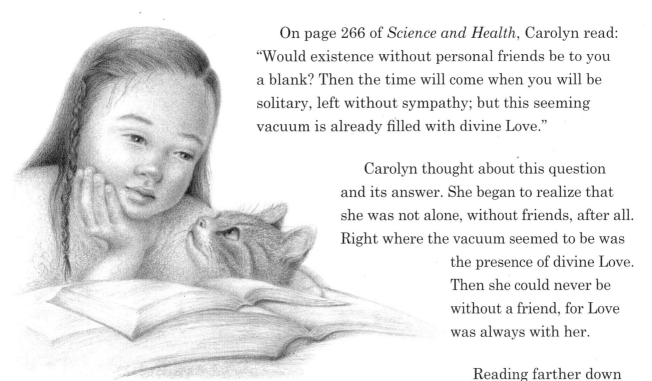

On page 266 of *Science and Health*, Carolyn read: "Would existence without personal friends be to you a blank? Then the time will come when you will be solitary, left without sympathy; but this seeming vacuum is already filled with divine Love."

Carolyn thought about this question and its answer. She began to realize that she was not alone, without friends, after all. Right where the vacuum seemed to be was the presence of divine Love. Then she could never be without a friend, for Love was always with her.

Reading farther down

on the same page, Carolyn found another statement, "Universal Love is the divine way in Christian Science."

Carolyn knew that *universal* means "including all." When we include everyone in our love, we are expressing universal, divine Love. Everybody becomes a friend.

Carolyn was finding the answer to her question, "What is a friend?" She wanted to tell someone about her discovery. She found her father in the garage at his workbench.

"Daddy, I think I know now what a friend really is!" she exclaimed, perching on a box.

Father looked up from his work. "Well, good! What is a friend?" he asked.

Carolyn frowned thoughtfully. "A friend is someone we love. And we can love everybody, so we can never really be without a friend."

Father nodded. "That's right. The Bible tells us that 'a friend loveth at all times' (Proverbs 17:17); so no matter how others treat us, a true friend never stops loving."

While Carolyn was getting ready for bed, she thought about her best friend. Denise was a good friend and would always be a good friend. But a best friend was someone very special. Finally Carolyn was beginning to realize who her best friend really was.

Mother came in to say good night. She was carrying the *Christian Science Hymnal.* "I just thought of a hymn that might be of help to you, dear," she said. She opened the *Hymnal* to No. 224 by John Ryland, and Carolyn read,

> O Lord, I would delight in Thee,
>   And on Thy care depend;
> To Thee in every trouble flee,
>   My best, my ever Friend.

Carolyn looked up at Mother and smiled. "Thank you, Mom," she said, "now I know who my best 'Friend' really is!"

The next day when Carolyn went out to play, all the children played together. For the first time in many weeks nobody was left out; nobody made a favorite of anybody. Since it was a very warm day, the children built a lemonade stand and sold lemonade to all the neighbors.

Carolyn was happy. She was no longer worried about finding and keeping a friend. She knew she would always have her best "Friend" with her. And as long as she expressed the Christly love which He gave her, she would never want for a friend.

—*Lucille Spangler Michener*

Originally published in the January 8, 1966, issue of the *Christian Science Sentinel*.

Sowing and Reaping: A Good Lesson for Every Life Problem

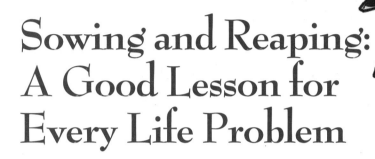

I'm Teresa, and my friend Alisa and I like to share ideas about God with each other. One time we were talking about sowing and reaping. The Bible talks about this, and we wanted to figure out how it could help us with our problems.

Sowing is when you plant and take care of seeds; reaping is when the seeds have grown into plants and it's harvesttime. The amount that you reap depends on how good a job you've done with sowing.

It's the same in our lives. If we do a good job with what God has given us, we will have the rewards of service to Him—joy, love, harmony.

Alisa pointed out that even before planting, you need to get the soil ready. We decided that this is like getting ourselves in a position to hear God better. Expressing love, calmness, readiness to listen, and forgiveness helps us to hear the thoughts from God that are always coming to us. On the other hand, hate, anger, and fear get in the way of listening to God. These stand for soil that doesn't allow for spiritual growth.

A parable from Jesus makes this exact point (see Luke 8:4–15). The story begins with a sower who went out to plant seeds. Some seeds fell on rocky ground, others fell on thorny ground, and others were eaten by birds. These seeds did not bring forth fruit. But the seed sown on good ground sprang up and produced a huge harvest! Jesus explained the meaning of each type of soil. The "good ground" stands for people with "an honest and good heart." These hearers of the word keep it, and "bring forth fruit with patience." This story helped Alisa and me see how important it is to take special care that we're planting in the right kind of soil.

This brings us to the second step in sowing, which is actually to plant the seed. Setting aside time to learn about and talk with God is very important. Also, we realized that it is helpful to be specific in our prayer. For instance, if you wanted to eat corn, you wouldn't plant the seed for a tomato plant. In much the same way, we can be exact with our thoughts. If we are praying about a certain problem, it is wise to listen to what God has to say about it. For example, if we had trouble understanding something in school, it would be helpful to pray to know that we're intelligent and reflect the Mind that is God. If we wanted something we could not afford, we could think about God's will and about how He helps us know what is right (or wrong) for us to have. Or, if we don't feel well, we could know that our health and freedom are God-given and permanent.

These ideas are powerful and practical. For us to use them well, we really have to let them grow in our thought, just the way we care for and tend young plants, and we have to be sure not to work in the wrong direction. Alisa and I looked at this statement in *Science and Health with Key to the Scriptures:* "The soil of disease is mortal mind, and you have an abundant or scanty crop of disease, according to the seedlings of fear. Sin and the fear of disease must be uprooted and cast out" (p. 188). This tells us to weed out any destructive and fearful thoughts, thoughts that lead to sickness. Doing so makes room for the good, strong thoughts that help and heal us.

Hand in hand with weeding is watering the seeds and watching them grow. Sometimes this takes time. So we need to be patient and persistent as we wait on God and trust His care. Jesus taught his disciples, "If ye continue in my word, then are ye my disciples indeed" (John 8:31). We need to keep building our faith and understanding until we see fruit.

After we have tilled, planted, weeded, watered, we can leave the whole thing in God's hands. And we can expect to enjoy His blessings at harvesttime. As long as we do a good job sowing, what we reap will be plentiful and good.

— Teresa K. Doan
and Alisa Nixon

Originally published in the August 23, 1999, issue of the *Christian Science Sentinel.*

God Is with Me Through the Night

God is with me through the night
See you in the morning light
All around me are His arms
Guarding me from any harm.

God is here and I am dear
God is Love—I cannot fear
See you in the morning light
God is with me through the night.

—*Kathryn Crosby Escruceria*

Originally published in the October 13, 1997, issue of the *Christian Science Sentinel*.

The Night Gracie's Ear Was Healed

Gracie was spending the night at Grandma's. They had lots of fun outside on the swing and playing checkers inside after the sun went down. Gracie loved having her grandma live nearby so that she could visit often. But, this night something different happened. Gracie got an earache. It was very uncomfortable, and no matter what Grandma said or did, it didn't feel any better.

Grandma knew a lot about God through reading the Bible and a book called *Science and Health with Key to the Scriptures*. Gracie had learned in Sunday School that these two books are like good friends. They help us know how to pray, and they explain to us the power of God's love that heals us.

Gracie and Grandma talked about how there were lots of people in the Bible who loved God and who listened to God. They must have known that real hearing has everything to do with listening to God. Noah listened to God to know how to build the ark that protected his family and the animals from the storm. Moses listened to God to know the rules called the Ten Commandments that keep us safe. David listened to God to know how to bring down big, scary Goliath. Like Goliath, the earache seemed big and scary to Gracie, too. But Gracie also remembered that Christ Jesus listened to God to know how to heal others, and he taught his followers how to heal.

Even though they couldn't get in touch with Mommy and Daddy right away, Grandma knew someone else they could call. She suggested that Gracie call a Christian Science practitioner to pray with them. A practitioner is someone who practices healing the way Jesus taught. The practitioner Gracie called told her that God was speaking to her, and, just like those in the Bible, she could really only hear what God was telling her. And God would only tell her that she is His perfect child and that she is completely safe from harm.

God is all good and never makes any hurt or evil. God is perfect, and, as His child, Gracie is perfect, too. Gracie did not have to listen to thoughts of fear. She could listen to what she knew was true about God and about herself as His obedient child.

After a while, Gracie's parents called to check in. When they heard that Gracie was not feeling well, they drove straight to Grandma's house to get her. On the way home, Gracie told her parents the truths of God she and the practitioner had talked about. The practitioner had also told her that God was her always present Father and Mother. No matter where she was, her Father-Mother God was right there with her, speaking to her. She could feel the power, strength, and might of her Father God. She could feel the sweet, tender touch of her Mother God. She could never be separated from the comfort of her divine Mother and Father, who is God. Not ever, not even for one second—not even for one snap of a finger—could she be without God's help. The practitioner had said, "God is always, always, always with you!" Gracie knew that she could never be shut off from her Father-Mother's care and that divine Love's powerful laws, not merely a mommy or a daddy, heal us.

Gracie's parents tucked her into bed and then sat with her, praying and sharing truths about God that they knew would help her. They knew it was time to be still, not to be upset or worried, and to listen to what God was telling all of them. This, they explained, was not just about waiting for a body to get better. It was about knowing the spiritual truths about God that bring quick healing. They were very calm because they had been healed many times through understanding truths of God. Gracie's parents, grandparents, and even her great-grandparents had relied on God for healing!

Gracie became still as she listened to her parents speak softly with each other about God's laws. She didn't understand all the words they were talking about, but she knew that the ideas were important. Her daddy said that because God is all good and fills all space, evil could have no cause. There is no imbalance in God's universe, no reaction, no virus, infection, or irritation. Gracie's mom opened *Science and Health* to page 7 and read this: "The 'divine ear' is not an auditory nerve. It is the all-hearing and all-knowing Mind, to whom each need of man is always known and by whom it will be supplied." There are only wide-open channels of truth, love, and goodness flowing between God and man. These channels are not fragile but are forever strong.

While her parents were sharing with each other, Gracie fell asleep. When she woke up the next morning, her ear had drained and was completely healed. All of them were grateful for what they had learned about real listening. That afternoon Gracie got to go back over to Grandma's for a happy hug and one more game of checkers!

—Jan Kassahn Keeler

Originally published in the March 23, 1998, issue of the *Christian Science Sentinel*.

The Mirror

Looking in a mirror
I see only me,
Not a scary monster,
Or a mango tree.
If I look much longer
I *still* see only me,
Not a ripe banana
Or a chickadee.

God's Science is a mirror,
The proper way to see
His world, and one another,
And *spiritual* me.
It shows me the right answers
And how thing *have* to be.
No evil in God's mirror,
But Love's reflection—me!

—*Kerry M. Knobelsdorff*

Originally published in the April 30, 1984, issue of the *Christian Science Sentinel*.

Julie Feels the Power of God

Julie crossed the moss-covered stone bridge which led into the park. Music from the park band mingled with the sounds of a rushing creek in the warm afternoon air. The family had hurried on ahead of her to find a picnic table on the green lawns, but Julie had lingered on the bridge. She watched the clear water splashing over smooth rocks below and almost wished she had not come. Even the promise Father had made that she and her brother, Jim, could go horseback riding didn't make her feel any better.

Coming down in the car, she hadn't felt well. Not wanting to spoil the family's day, she had said nothing about it. But now Julie felt that she must lie down, so she joined the others on the wide expanse of lawns.

Her father and Jim had gone off to see the animals, for the park had a small zoo. Mother and Grandma were busy putting out the lunch on a picnic table under the wide spreading branches of an oak tree. Julie lay down on the cool grass. She had not brought her copy of either the Bible or the Christian Science textbook, *Science and Health with Key to the Scriptures* by Mrs. Eddy, and for a moment she felt lost without them. Then she remembered something her teacher had said just that morning in the Christian Science Sunday School. "The truths you learn and make your own, you can take with you wherever you go."

She realized that there were many truths she had learned from reading the Bible and *Science and Health* both at home and in Sunday School. She thought of them now. She thoughtfully repeated the Lord's Prayer, which Christ Jesus gave us, and "the scientific statement of being" from *Science and Health*. This statement begins with the words, "There is no life, truth, intelligence, nor substance in matter" (p. 468).

Then Julie remembered a statement from the textbook. Her brother had been memorizing it for Sunday School, and she had learned it just by listening to him say it every night. It reads: "There is no power apart from God. Omnipotence has all-power, and to acknowledge any other power is to dishonor God" (p. 228).

Julie thought about this. Since God is All and fills all space, there can be no other power or presence. Since God is good, His power is good.

Then what was it that seemed to be able to make her sick? It was not good, therefore not of God. And if not of God, then it must be unreal, untrue. Evil, or error, is the belief that there can be power apart from God. It is the belief that life and intelligence can be in matter. The textbook says of evil, "Evil has no power, no intelligence, for God is good, and therefore good is infinite, is All" (pp. 398–399).

God comes to us quietly, gently. He sends us angel thoughts of good which are all-powerful because they come from Him. The omnipotence of good destroys the belief in an evil, destructive power.

As Julie lay on the grass she was surprised to find how busy she was, even without her books, thinking of many truths she had learned in Christian Science. She knew that man is spiritual, made in the image and likeness of God, expressing His goodness and power. She would not, then, see herself as subject to any other supposed power. She would not accept sickness as a part of His creation. She would not dishonor Him by believing He could send sickness to His children. She would not dishonor Him by believing she could be sick.

Just then Mother noticed her lying on the grass. "Is something wrong, Julie?" she asked.

Julie sat up. "I wasn't feeling very well, but I feel much better now!" she replied.

Julie helped Mother and Grandma set the table with plastic plates and cups and put out the sandwiches.

"I'm glad you're better," Mother said, pouring the lemonade. "Can I help you?"

"What was that Bible quotation you told me the other night when we were talking?" Julie asked.

"It was from the ninety-first Psalm," Mother answered and repeated it to Julie: "Because thou hast made the Lord, which is my refuge, even the most High, thy habitation; there shall no evil befall thee, neither shall any plague come nigh thy dwelling. For he shall give his angels charge over thee, to keep thee in all thy ways" (Psalms 91:9–11).

Julie smiled. "Yes, that's it."

Suddenly she felt glad, for she knew and felt God's ever-presence. He had sent His angel thoughts to her to help her when she needed them.

"I think I'll go find Father and Jim," she said.

"Good! Tell them lunch is ready. Maybe afterward you can go for that horseback ride!"

As Julie followed the winding path to the park zoo, she felt that she had learned something more about her Father-Mother God. It didn't matter whether she was at home or in a park, whether she had her books or not, she moved forever in His goodness, in His presence and power.

In the distance she saw Father and Jim watching a lazy lion sleeping peacefully in his cage, and she ran quickly to catch up with them.

—Lucille Spangler Michener

Originally published in the May 14, 1966, issue of the *Christian Science Sentinel*.

Dear *Sentinel*,

I had just finished playing tennis with my sister and her friend, and was getting into my mom's car. I didn't realize that my hand was still in the car door when the friend closed the door all the way on my fingers. I yelled, and my mom had to reach over quickly from her seat to open the door. My hand really hurt and I started crying. Right away Mom started saying that there are no accidents in God's kingdom.

When we got home a few minutes later, Mom and I went into the living room. Mom brought her *Science and Health with Key to the Scriptures,* a dictionary, and another book I didn't know—a Concordance to the writings of Mary Baker Eddy. She read from *Science and Health* about accidents, and I started praying with her. We knew that there are no accidents in God's kingdom, and that I couldn't be outside of God's kingdom. Since God is spiritual and I am His reflection, I am spiritual, too. No material accident could touch me.

Soon I felt perfect. That night I had an important baseball playoff game and was able to hit a double with the bases loaded! My hand didn't hurt at all.

> — *John Raffles*
> *Lake Forest, Illinois*

When the car door closed, John had four fingers of one hand caught in the hinge. I knew right then that we had to choose between believing an accident had taken place (as the physical senses were shouting) or holding to the reality of John's unharmed perfection, as a spiritual idea, and the reality of the kingdom of God, good. When we got home, we looked up the word *accident* in the Concordance to Mrs. Eddy's writings. In *Science and Health,* we found the sentence "Accidents are unknown to God, or immortal Mind, and we must leave the mortal basis of belief and unite with the one Mind, in order to change the notion of chance to the proper sense of God's unerring direction and thus bring out harmony" (p. 424). I also called John's father at work for his prayerful support.

Earlier in the week, I had been studying another passage from *Science and Health* that reads, "Willingness to become as a little child and to leave the old for the new, renders thought receptive of the advanced idea" (pp. 323–324). This was a great opportunity to share childlike trust, and the purity of John's thought enabled him to realize healing very quickly. Within an hour of the incident John was happily playing, showing no evidence of injury, and clearly capable of playing baseball that evening.

— Catherine Raffles

Originally published in the August 23, 1999, issue of the *Christian Science Sentinel*.

Shine, Shine, Shine

Have you ever seen
A big, dark cloud
Covering the sun?

And all at once,
A ray of light
Shines through

As if to say,
Happy day!
No cloud can hide *me*.

Just that way
No clouds of trouble
Can hide God's child.

You're like a ray of sunshine
Always at one
With your Father-Mother God.

And safe in
His protecting care—
In truth, always happy, healthy, perfect.

So see those cloud thoughts
As nothing—having no place or power—
And shine, shine, shine (see Isaiah 60:1).

—*Mary Jo Beebe*

Originally published in the October 5, 1998, issue of the *Christian Science Sentinel.*

Topher Returns to Love

Topher loves to go skating. Many afternoons one winter when his little sister was napping, he went skating with his friend Riggs from his pre-kindergarten class and Riggs's mommy. One day, two other friends, Chelsea and Dylan, came along, too. Riggs spent a lot of time skating with Dylan, and Topher felt hurt. He told Riggs in a mad way that he thought that Riggs wasn't being nice.

By the time they went home, Topher was crying. Topher told his mom the whole story and ended by saying that Riggs was not his friend anymore. Two days later Topher still felt the same way.

Finally, Topher's mom said, "Have you ever thought of forgiving and forgetting?" Topher was quiet for a long time. Then his mommy asked, "What does forgiving and forgetting mean to you, Topher?" He said slowly and thoughtfully, "Well, forgiving means returning to love, and forgetting is forgetting that it ever happened."

Topher's mommy gave him a big hug and said those were beautiful words. She asked him if he had heard these good words at Sunday School. He said no. He just thought them. She told him that these were thoughts from God coming to him.

Topher's mommy told him that listening to God heals hurt feelings. She said that one of Jesus' disciples, Peter, asked Jesus how many times he should forgive. Peter wondered, should he forgive someone seven times? But Jesus said he should forgive "seventy times seven" (see Matthew 18:21, 22). That's a lot! But that just shows how great God's love for us is. He never stops loving us, and His love never runs out. So we can just keep on forgiving, or returning to love, because God's love is always there to turn to.

Later that night, Topher had a chance to practice what he had just learned about forgiving and forgetting. He didn't want to go to bed, and his daddy told him that he had to. In the end, Topher cried, and his daddy stomped down the stairs in a mad way. Topher sat in his room, angry.

A few minutes later, Topher's daddy came back upstairs. "Mommy said I should come ask you what you learned about forgiving and forgetting today," he said. At first, Topher didn't want to tell him. He still felt mad. Then he burst into a smile and said, "Forgiving is returning to love, and forgetting is forgetting that it ever happened." That made Topher's daddy smile really big now, too. They forgave each other and forgot all about their argument right then and there and shared a big hug.

Now Topher was ready to forgive Riggs, too. Topher and Riggs have been great buddies ever since, and they still love to go skating together. Sometimes their other friends come along, too, and they all have fun together.

—*Molly Mary Virginia Larsen*

Originally published in the March 15, 1999, issue of the *Christian Science Sentinel*.

Everyone Can Be a Knight in Shining Armor

Tucked away in a quiet corner of the Metropolitan Museum of Art in New York City lies a vast, soaring hall where footsteps seem to echo down the centuries and a silent army of warriors stands forever on guard. This gallery, where armor from many different lands and historical periods is displayed, is one of my favorite exhibits. I love to look at the beautifully crafted swords, shields, and suits of armor. You can take a peek at the collection on the museum's website or check out a book on the subject at your local library. You can also read about armor in the Bible.

Remember the story of David and Goliath? (see I Samuel, chap. 17.) Goliath must have been a terrifying sight. First of all, he was huge—bigger than Michael Jordan or any other basketball player who has been in the big leagues. And, as a member of the Philistine army, he was a trained soldier, dressed in the very latest high-tech gear of his time. His armor had a helmet to protect his neck and the sides of his face, a very heavy coat of mail (made from iron or steel) that covered his chest, and greaves of brass (like soccer shinguards made from metal) that covered his legs. He looked unbeatable! That's probably why the army of Israel was afraid of him.

One person wasn't impressed by Goliath, though. The shepherd boy David had come to the battlefield to see his older brothers, who were soldiers. He saw the giant, heard his threats, and went straight to King Saul. "Let no man's heart fail because of him," David said; "thy servant will go and fight with this Philistine" (verse 32). Eventually, King Saul agreed to let David fight, and even gave him his own royal armor to wear. David tried it on, but it was very heavy. He wasn't used to this kind of armor, so he decided not to wear it. Instead, he went to face Goliath with his trusty sling and a handful of stones.

But David wore another kind of armor that day—spiritual armor. He told the giant, "Thou comest to me with a sword, and with a spear, and with a shield: but I come to thee in the name of the Lord of hosts, the God of the armies of Israel…" (verse 45). Next he used his sling to hurl a stone at Goliath, hitting him in just about the only place that was unprotected—his forehead. David found the weak spot in Goliath's armor and toppled him.

What was it that kept David safe and helped him triumph over this frightening enemy? It was the spiritual armor of David's faith in God. Centuries later, Paul described this kind of armor perfectly. He called it "the whole armour of God," which he explained was made of spiritual qualities—the "breastplate of righteousness," the "shield of faith," the "helmet of salvation," and the "sword of the Spirit, which is the word of God" (Ephesians 6:13–17). David went forth to meet Goliath wearing "the whole armour of God." That's what protected him on the battlefield.

You can wear this same armor and be protected just as David was. Mary Baker Eddy explains how this armor works. She says, "Good thoughts are an impervious armor; clad therewith you are completely shielded from the attacks of error of every sort" *(The First Church of Christ, Scientist, and Miscellany,* p. 210). If something is impervious, absolutely nothing can go through it. Our spiritual armor of good thoughts keeps us safe from fears or worries that would "attack" us by trying to tell us that we're not feeling well or that we're lonely, scared, or sad. When we listen only to God and the good thoughts He sends us, we are wearing our spiritual armor and are entirely safe.

There are many ways to arm yourself with good thoughts. You can read and think about the truths in the Bible, for one. I like to read the Bible Lesson in the *Christian Science Quarterly* every day. It's made up of verses from the Bible and sentences from the Christian Science textbook, *Science and Health with Key to the Scriptures* by Mrs. Eddy. The Lesson always gives me new ideas to add to my spiritual armor. Also, Sunday School is a great place to learn what spiritual ideas other kids use for armor and to share the ones you use. And, of course, no matter where you are, you can always listen quietly to God for the pure ideas He is giving each of us all the time. These ideas shield us when we face our own "Goliaths"—any problems that try to bully us into believing that something is more powerful than God, who is good.

One morning, a boy named Ian woke up with a really bad headache, one that seemed as big as Goliath. He and his mom had talked about spiritual armor before. She reminded him that there were no chinks, or cracks, in his armor, so nothing could get into his thinking to hurt him. He was always safe in God's care. After his brother left for school, Ian and his mom read that week's Bible Lesson. They discussed how listening to and understanding the word of God shielded him from any sickness or discomfort. Before long the headache completely disappeared. Ian's teacher and friends were surprised and glad when he came to school later that morning.

Isn't it great that our spiritual armor of good thoughts doesn't weigh a thing, since we always want to have it on? Mrs. Eddy says to "keep your minds so filled with Truth and Love, that sin, disease, and death cannot enter them" *(Miscellany,* p. 210). She goes on to say: "It is plain that nothing can be added to the mind already full. There is no door through which evil can enter, and no space for evil to fill in a mind filled with goodness."

When you keep your thoughts filled with God's thoughts, you are wearing your armor. And no bad thoughts can come in. Your armor will shield you. You're always safe with God.

— Heather Vogel Frederick

Originally published in the October 23, 2000, issue of the *Christian Science Sentinel.*

Not an Echo

Grandma was visiting us, and she asked me what I wanted to be when I grew up. "A Christian Science practitioner like you," I said. (That means she helped people through prayer when they asked her to. She understood how prayer heals, and her name was listed in *The Christian Science Journal*.) Grandma smiled and said I didn't have to wait until I was big to begin to learn how to be a Christian Science practitioner. "Start right now," she said.

I must have looked surprised because she asked me to bring her my "books" (she meant my Bible and *Science and Health with Key to the Scriptures* by Mrs. Eddy—I had my own set, red ones). I got them, and she showed me the Cross and Crown seal on the front of *Science and Health,* with what Jesus said written around it— "Heal the sick • Raise the dead • Cleanse the lepers • Cast out demons" (see Matthew 10:8). Then she showed me a place inside *Science and Health* where Mrs. Eddy says children can heal too (see page 37, lines 22–25).

"What you know of God right now is enough to heal," she told me. "But you have to *know* it, not just *say* it. An echo repeats the words; but you must understand what the words actually *mean,* and that heals." Then she asked me, "What *do* you know of God?"

That was easy. "Well, He's Love. I know that." (That's the very first thing I learned in Sunday School.) "And He's everywhere." I could've gone on and on, but Grandma stopped me.

"Even that's enough to heal, so all-powerful is God," Grandma told me. "But you must *know* it, not just echo the words. Think about what that means to you. Think about it all the time, and let the way you act show that you know God is all-powerful, and you'll be a good healer. Not just an echo."

That night before bed I played Sunday School. I put all my dolls around me in a semicircle on the floor, and I showed them the Cross and Crown seal on *Science and Health*. I told them all the things Grandma had told me and all about God's love and care for all of His creation and that they could never find themselves in any trouble where He was not right there with them to help.

"So," I said, "if you're ever feeling scared or sick or sad or mad or worried, just stop right there and know God's love for you is so much bigger than those feelings! And when you love and trust God more than anything and see that He made all His children good and perfect like Him, then you won't be afraid or sick or bad any longer. Because when you know what is really true, healing comes. Remember, you're not echoes. You're healers." Mom overheard me, and when she tucked me in later, she told me I was a good little Christian Science practitioner.

But just a few days later when I was at school, I felt very sick, and my teacher sent me to the school nurse. The nurse called Mom to come and take me home. I heard her tell Mom I had scarlet fever.

This was my big chance to heal! All the way home Mom sang a hymn to me about God's "gentle presence." (It was Hymn 207 in the *Christian Science Hymnal,* and the words are by Mrs. Eddy.) When we got home, I crawled into bed with my Bible and *Science and Health* and tried to feel God's "gentle presence" around me, but I didn't seem to be able to do that very much. Grandma came to visit and gave me a big hug, but I just cried. "I thought I knew God, but I'm only an echo," I told her.

"Oh no, you're not just an echo," she said firmly. "You are God's child. You *do* understand God! This is one of those times when you need to *know* you understand Him." She explained: "You can understand God because He is divine Mind and is right here, giving you every thought you need to comfort you and make you strong." Grandma was always so sure of God's love, and it showed in her face and in her voice and in everything about her. I felt God's love then, too, and it comforted me.

"You have God's authority to know Him," Grandma said. "Everything you've learned of Him in the Bible—that He's here now, that He is almighty and all good—all of this truth God has given you. God's truth heals. And anything else is a lie and has no power at all."

Before Grandma left she showed me this verse in the Bible: "God is in the midst of her;

she shall not be moved: God shall help her, and that right early" (Psalms 46:5).

"That's God's promise to you right here, right now," she told me. "God is helping you know that He has made you perfect and good forever." Then she gave my hand a little squeeze and said, "Think about it."

So I did. It made me feel all settled and happy to know God is always right where I am. So I couldn't be "moved"—made to forget His love. And "right early" meant "now" to me. I remember that I fell asleep thinking about God's loving care of all His children.

The next morning I was completely well and got ready for school. But Mom explained that I couldn't go, because the law said I had to stay home from school a certain number of days because of that sickness. So even though I wasn't sick anymore, we obeyed the law and I stayed home. My teacher sent my homework home, and I did it. I made cookies with Mom and got to talk to my friend Janice on the phone after school.

And I played Sunday School with my dolls. Here's what I told them: "I learned something important about healing—Sometimes when you need and want so much to know that God is All, it can seem like just words. If that happens, you can stop right then and there, and know that the truth you've learned about God from the Bible has come from God! So of course it's true, and you can prove that the truth is true.

"Remember to stay close to God—keep knowing and trusting and loving Him all the time. Then you'll feel God's love all around you—and God's love heals. How do I know all this? Grandma told me, and I just proved it myself."

—*Judith Hardy Olson*

Originally published in the May 25, 1992, issue of the *Christian Science Sentinel*.

Robby's Unplanned Trip

For the last few days of summer vacation Peter was visiting his grandparents in the country. Their home was a small red cottage with lots of maple trees around that were good for climbing. Peter loved to go there and play with Robby, a handsome green and blue parakeet that lived with Grandma and Grandpa. Robby had the freedom of the house and only went into his cage to eat or sleep.

He chased anything that moved, especially the vacuum cleaner. He liked to sit on that while Grandma whirred it around the carpet. Chattering endlessly was another of his accomplishments. His most-used and loudest expression was, "Come-on-Robby, come-on!"

One warm evening Peter asked Grandma if they could eat on the patio. Now, Robby's favorite place to perch usually was on the back of Grandpa's collar. But this time he chose Peter's collar. Peter didn't know Robby was there; he was so light, and Peter was busy setting the table and chatting. Nobody noticed Robby when he flew up into a nearby tree.

After supper, Grandma, Grandpa, and Peter decided to go to the beach for a swim. They carefully closed all doors to the house and drove off. They didn't know little Robby had been locked out.

Returning home, Grandma went to cover the bird's cage and found it empty. A quick search showed he wasn't in the house. They all realized what must have happened. Hurrying outdoors they called and called, "Robby." But there was no answer, so they sadly closed up the house for the night, leaving the patio light on and the cage outside.

Right away Peter felt it was his fault. He should have been more alert. After so many hours the tiny bird was probably gone forever. A high wind had come up, and Robby was used to living in a warm, cozy house. Other birds or animals might harm him!

Peter didn't stay sad very long. He went to his room to pray. He remembered that only two weeks ago his class in the Christian Science Sunday School had been questioning how and where animals fit into God's vast creation. During that discussion the teacher asked Peter to read Mrs. Eddy's words, "God is the Life, or intelligence, which forms and preserves the individuality and identity of animals as well as of men" (*Science and Health with Key to the Scriptures,* p. 550).

It occurred to Peter that if God, good, is the Life of every living thing, nothing bad could possibly reach their little bird. How could it? Satisfied that his missing friend was being directed by divine intelligence, Peter wasn't afraid anymore. Leaving everything in God's loving care, he crawled into bed and slept soundly.

The next morning Peter was wakened by the happy chirping of many different birds that live in the trees surrounding the cottage. He jumped out of bed and ran to see if Robby had come back. No, he hadn't. The cage was still empty. But this couldn't shake Peter's faith in the power of good, and he continued to pray.

Grandma came out on the patio. "Peter," she said, "let's say the ninety-first Psalm." Peter liked this part best: "He shall cover thee with his feathers, and under his wings shalt thou trust... . Thou shalt not be afraid for the terror by night; nor for the arrow that flieth by day" (Psalms 91:4, 5). It was just what Peter needed—to hear that *wherever* Robby was, the wings of divine Love were over him.

And then Peter heard, from the chorus of morning bird songs, one voice higher and more persistent than the rest. He yelled, "Robby, Robby." And back came the answer: "Come-on-Robby, come-on!" That fearless little bird kept answering each time Peter called his name until Peter was able to trace his voice across the road and high up into a large tree.

Twice (as though to show his joy in being found) Robby swooped down over the housetop and soared up again into his overnight shelter, the high tree. At last he flew down and landed gently on Peter's outstretched hand.

You couldn't find a more grateful family anywhere. God's tender care for all of His creation had made possible the safe return of this tiny pet from his unplanned trip.

—Mary Elizabeth Barton

Originally published in the August 10, 1981, issue of the *Christian Science Sentinel*.

James Helps Out

One day Mom came to pick me up from a friend's house. When we were walking home, she said she didn't feel well. As soon as we were in our house, Mom lay down on the sofa. My little sister Anna and I were hungry, so Mom asked me to find a snack that we could share.

We had fun. I used a step stool to get the snack. I picked out some cottage cheese and found a spoon. Anna thought it was funny to have me feed her, and we laughed a lot.

Soon we were thirsty. It was hard to get cups because they are in a cabinet way up high. I went into the living room to ask Mom for some help, but she still couldn't get up. Back in the kitchen, I found clean cups in the dishwasher. While I fixed our drinks, I remembered how Mom looked. She needed help, too.

I knew how I could help. I could pray for Mom. I have been learning how to pray at the Christian Science Sunday School. Our teacher tells us about Christ Jesus in the Bible. He healed people because he knew that God is Love; God loves us all. The teacher also reads to us from another book, *Science and Health with Key to the Scriptures* by Mary Baker Eddy. This book tells us how Christ Jesus healed. Like the disciples, we can learn to heal, too. I know this because I was healed of both a fever and an upset stomach when my family and I prayed.

When I thought about Mom, I remembered one of the things my dad reads to me from the Bible: "I will say of the Lord, He is my refuge and my fortress: my God; in him will I trust" (Psalms 91:2). This reminded me how good and powerful God is. I know I can trust Him to keep me safe all the time.

I also remembered a prayer I had learned in Sunday School: "God guides, guards, and governs thee." I like this prayer and the Bible verse. They tell me there isn't anything that can put me outside of God's goodness. I knew that Mom was all right because she is always safe with God, too.

Anna and I went back into the living room. Mom was sitting up and had a very happy look on her face. She smiled and gave me a big kiss. Then she went into the kitchen to fix dinner. I felt good because I could use what I'm learning about God to help my mom.

Parent's note: When we arrived home, I was in pain and felt very weak. I felt I should try to reach my husband to ask him to pray for me, but I couldn't make the call. Lying on the sofa and listening to the children giggling over the cottage cheese and their drinks, I felt enough peace that I could sleep. I was asleep only a matter of minutes when I heard the spiritual message "Get up; you can do your work now." These words of inspiration came with such conviction that I sat right up. James told me later that he had been praying. His prayer had affirmed that God was present with us at that very moment, and I was literally awakened to realize that in the presence of God, who is All, nothing could overpower me or obstruct my right activity. As God's spiritual expression, I could never be separated from Him.

I was soon at work preparing dinner totally free of pain. In *Science and Health* Mrs. Eddy says, "It is possible,—yea, it is the duty and privilege of every child, man, and woman,—to follow in some degree the example of the Master by the demonstration of Truth and Life, of health and holiness" (p. 37). This explains for me why it was very natural for James to respond to my need with the truths he is learning at Sunday School and at home.

—*James Hegarty and
Janet Ivcich Hegarty*

Originally published in the January 16, 1995, issue of the *Christian Science Sentinel*.

Dear *Sentinel,*

One night while I was sleeping, I kept getting awful nightmares. When I woke from my sleep, I was scared. I fell back asleep, thinking the nightmares would just vanish, but they didn't. That's when it occurred to me that I had to do more than just fall back asleep. I had to turn to God for a real answer. I asked myself if God would ever put bad thoughts in my thinking, and, of course, the answer was no. I prayed to know this, and I prayed to know that I was protected from things that would scare or harm me. Beside my bed I have a verse from Psalms that say, "I will both lie down in peace, and sleep; for You alone, O Lord, make me dwell in safety" (The New King James Version, Psalms 4:8). Knowing this, I fell back asleep, and the nightmares did vanish.

—Melissa Patterson

Originally published in the October 23, 2000, issue of the *Christian Science Sentinel.*

The House with the Colored Windows

Dick and Dorothy had recently moved to a farm on a hillside, and were delighted to find, on the very top of the hill, a small summerhouse in which they could play. From this little summerhouse one could look out over the whole world below, or so it seemed, and in the near distance were fields of corn and a stretch of pasture land where a white horse grazed contentedly.

Now a feature of the summerhouse was a series of windows, one of red glass, one yellow, one green, and one blue. The fifth and last window was of the usual type, clear and transparent.

One day, when the children were playing on the top of the hill, Dick heard Dorothy cry out, "Come and see the red horse!" Incredulous, Dick came running into the house where his sister was standing before the red window, looking out at "Whitie."

"I don't see any red horse," he said; then, catching the spirit of the fun, he said, "But I do see a big green one!" Where do you suppose he was standing? Of course—in front of the green window!

The game continued. They both saw a yellow horse when they looked from the yellow window. And when they looked through the blue window, of course they saw a blue horse. Indeed, the whole landscape seemed to take on the color of the pane of glass through which they saw it.

"But this nice clear window makes everything all right again," Dick declared. "It's our own 'Whitie' after all. I had begun to think I'd have to scrub his color off, and give him a coat of whitewash." And he chuckled to himself.

Dorothy, however, was not listening, for it had suddenly occurred to her that there was a lesson in their little play, a lesson to help them in Christian Science. Both children attended the Christian Science Sunday School, where they were learning about the real man. Sometimes it had seemed to her that there was also another "man," who was often unhappy or sick or cross. Sometimes it had been hard to find and see the real man of God's creating.

"Why, it's just like the horse and the windows!" she explained to Dick and Mother at lunch time. "You see, there was only one horse, and he was white. There never was a red horse or a blue one or one of any other color in the pasture."

"Yes," agreed her brother. "What made us think we saw four or five different horses was the place from which we were looking. I know that if we stand in the right place—that is, with Principle—and look with spiritual sense, we can't help seeing what is really there."

Their mother smiled. "You saw the real white horse through that last window, didn't you? What are some of the qualities that clear window has? Perhaps if we try to reflect these qualities—purity and transparent goodness—we shall reflect the spiritual vision that sees things as they really are."

"For one thing," Dick said thoughtfully, "the last window wasn't 'colored' by any mortal mind beliefs. It was a clean, spotless window, too, Mother, or else we should have seen a speckled horse!"

Then their mother sent the little boy to find a reference in *Science and Health with Key to the Scriptures,* and when he had found it he read it aloud: "Jesus beheld in Science the perfect man, who appeared to him where sinning mortal man appears to mortals. In this perfect man the Saviour saw God's own likeness, and this correct view of man healed the sick" (pp. 476–477).

"Oh, I see," said Dorothy. "It's like that Bible verse, '…now we see through a glass, darkly, but then face to face…'" (I Corinthians 13:12).

"Just one more thing," said Mother. "What did you children have to do to that red horse to make him white again?"

Both looked at her in complete amazement. Then they realized she was helping them to find still another lesson.

"Do to him?" queried Dick. "But, Mother, there never was any red horse! Oh! Then there really never was any sick or unhappy person, either. And we don't have to change the sick person or unhappy person that seems to be; we only have to look at him from the right standpoint. Isn't that it, Mother?"

"Yes, indeed. And seeing the true man in this way is seeing our brother as God gives us to see him. We can never see God's image and likeness by using our material senses, for they are like the colored windows—all deceivers. We must see everything and everybody as God knows them. I think I'll join you tomorrow on your hilltop and we'll look at each other through the different panes of glass. Won't that be fun?"

Dorothy agreed that she would love to see a green Dick or a blue Mother, as long as she knew they were not real.

"And then we'll take a long look out over the universe and remember that we must always see it as perfect and eternal, as God-created and God-protected," continued Mother. "Yes, I think we shall all become world workers if we continue to keep in thought our lesson of the house with the colored windows."

And then, while Dick and Dorothy gathered close to her, she took her copy of *Miscellaneous Writings 1883–1896* by Mrs. Eddy and read these words from page 330: "The alders bend over the streams to shake out their tresses in the water-mirrors; let mortals bow before the creator, and, looking through Love's transparency, behold man in God's image and likeness, arranging in the beauty of holiness each budding thought."

—Virginia Haynes

Originally published in the January 1, 1944, issue of the *Christian Science Sentinel*.

Anyone Can Pray—Including You

It was time to walk home from school. And I was feeling afraid again.

I used to love the walk. In the fall there were many-colored leaves to scuff through or pick up. In winter, snow-covered shapes were funny or mysterious, and sometimes ice decorated every branch and twig. Spring was best of all, with its sweet fragrances and new green shoots.

But this spring things were different. A big boy had begun hiding behind a tree after school, waiting for the youngest children to pass by. Then he would charge at us with his head down, like an angry bull. He made frightening sounds, too. Every day we scattered and ran in fear.

I had attended Sunday School since I was two years old. On its wall were written the words "God is Love." In class we learned we could always trust God to love and care for us. I thought about this. To trust God is to be unafraid. But how could I be unafraid right in the middle of what seemed to be such a fearful situation? I didn't know the answer to this question yet, but I did know I could find it by praying.

A great thing about praying is that anyone, anywhere, can do it—including a six-year-old, like I was then. Some people call it "talking with God," some do a kind of "listening" to God in their thinking, and others think of God and His ideas in a very logical way called "reasoning." No matter how we pray, when prayer starts with God, we find the help we need.

My thinking about God—my prayer—went something like this: God is good. He made everyone good, just like Him. God, Love, is present with all His children. So each of us expresses His love. No one can be outside this Love or act unloving. God keeps all of us safe and happy.

A pretty simple prayer, but just right for me. Now I knew I could look at every child on my walk home as the child of Love—even the bully. I could refuse to see myself and my friends as frightened, and the big boy as scary. In doing this, I would be trusting God.

Words from a hymn we sang in Sunday School had always comforted me:

> I walk with Love along the way,
> And O, it is a holy day;
> No more I suffer cruel fear,
> I feel God's presence with me here;
> The joy that none can take away
> Is mine; I walk with Love today.
> (*Christian Science Hymnal*, Minny M. H. Ayers, No. 139)

As I added this verse to my prayer, I stopped feeling so scared. I began to feel sure we could all "walk with Love" on the way home.

When I approached the tree the next day, I was able to walk quietly on, trying my best to see Love's children right there on the sidewalk. And a wonderful thing happened. The chasing decreased, and the boy acted much friendlier. Very soon he stopped his threatening actions completely. We never talked about it. The wrong activity just ended, and walking home became fun again.

When we pray, we are guided. God helps us know how to act or what to do. That usually includes telling a parent, or an adult you can trust, if someone is acting in a bad way. In my case, praying made it clear that I could continue walking home safely. This is another wonderful thing about prayer—it results in help that's a perfect fit for our needs. It shows us *how* God keeps us safe—by giving us His loving, wise thoughts.

Can you pray about something that seems scary or wrong? Definitely. You can always listen for thoughts from God or remember good things you've learned about Him and His creation. You can reason by starting with God's allness and love for you. You can refuse to see or believe anything unlike Him to be true.

Can your age get in the way of your prayer? No. The seeming "bigness" of the problem you face? No. Your experience? No. *Nothing* can. Prayer is unstoppable. After all, it calls on the one supreme, ever-present power, God, whose very child *you are*.

—*Cheryl F. Ranson*

Originally published in the September 6, 1999, issue of the *Christian Science Sentinel*.

Forgiveness

On the way home from Palestine, Texas, I let my sister Tara play with my tape player. I told her to be careful and not to break it. I'd had a tape player in the past, but this was the best one I had ever had. She played with it and fell asleep in the car.

After we got home, we decided to go have a picnic with some friends for Easter. We ate hamburgers and cake. While we were eating, Tara pulled out my tape player and started listening to music. I got mad and complained to my parents that Tara brought the tape player without my permission. Then I told Tara: "You'll break it. Give it to me." I still let her listen to the music, though.

Later, everyone decided to go feed the ducks at a pond nearby. Tara had the tape player in her hand and started walking over with us to the pond. Suddenly, the tape player slipped from Tara's hand and fell into the pond. I watched it sink to the bottom. I felt as if I were going to explode with anger, and I cried out a big grunt of anger. I ran to the picnic benches and told my mother what happened.

Then I thought about Christ Jesus and how he was so forgiving, and how anger or fear didn't get in the way of his loving others. I thought about how we were trying to be more like him every day in following his teachings. He listened to God and healed the sick.

I also thought about how material things are not what's really important. They can be lost. But Love, God, is always there. Loving thoughts are the important things, because that's how we heal and help each other every day. A tape player could not destroy the love and peace between my sister and me. My sister and I have everlasting love that can't be destroyed by a material item. We are God's children, His expression.

I went over to Tara and said: "Tara, it's no big deal. Don't feel bad, because it's not what's really important."

Tara told me that she was a bad person. I said: "Tara, you are *not* bad. Don't feel guilty. It does not matter. What matters is that you are OK and that our relationship isn't destroyed."

After that Tara and I had fun and didn't let anything else ruin our day.

—Ashley Wolfe

Parent's note: When Ashley came storming back to us and announced that her sister had dropped her tape player into the pond, she was upset. Within a few minutes, however, we noticed her back at the pond with her arm around her sister, patting her and appearing to comfort her. She was perfectly free from that moment on. It wasn't until she wrote about the experience later that afternoon and asked me to read it, that I knew about the healing that had taken place in her thought.

Earlier that weekend she had lost a silver charm bracelet, and we thought it had been dropped when she had taken a walk in the woods. Monday when I called a relative to tell her to watch for the bracelet, she called back within a few minutes to say she had walked straight to the couch, looked under a cushion, and there was the bracelet.

I know Ashley's total freedom from any sense of loss having to do with the tape player paved the way for the recovery of the bracelet. I am so grateful that both children have learned to turn to God in time of trouble and pray with confidence to their Father-Mother God.

—Vicki L. Wolfe

Originally published in the April 28, 1997, issue of the *Christian Science Sentinel*.

Go Forward

"Go forward," God said.
Though enemies pursued
And deep seas roared,
On I went, God led.

At waters' edge, I paused,
While Truth divided the seas
And revealed a safe, dry path
On which I quickly crossed.

God keeps us in the right direction
If we just trust and listen.
Keep your hand in His
And feel the sweet protection.

*Exodus 14:15: "And the Lord said unto Moses,
Wherefore criest thou unto me? speak unto the
children of Israel, that they go forward: ... ."*

—*Carolyn Nutwell*

Originally published in the July 16, 2001, issue of the *Christian Science Sentinel*.

Love's Refuge

A dad from Emporia, Kansas, wrote this version of the 91st Psalm for his daughter Katie when she was having problems with some of the kids at school:

———————

I live in Love's refuge. I will not be afraid of what others might say about me. God, who is divine Love, delivers me from frightening thoughts. He keeps my thoughts from falling into a deep hole so that I can and will walk before Him in His light. God will deliver me from the traps of gossip and lies. He will cover me with His feathers—His holy messages—and keep me safe, loved.

God's love is my shield. Because I'm wrapped in this love, the arrows of envy bounce off me. I won't be afraid of the night's terror—dreams and puffed-up dragons— of the day's hurts. No evil can reach me. No fear can enter where I live—the calm of God's fortress. God has set me on a high hill, far above hate. Because I know and call on God's name, His power is always with me. He will pick me up if I trip and fall.

I call on God, and He answers me with angels, His inspirations. God is with me in hard times. He will deliver me and honor me. God is my Father-Mother, my Shepherd who watches over me and guides me in all that I do. I am grateful to God and will honor Him with great joy.

—Terry Barham

Originally published in the February 26, 2001, issue of the *Christian Science Sentinel*.

Morning and Night

In the morning ...

Thank you, God, for Your presence this day,
For all the good You will send my way.
In my work and in my play,
Your angels will be with me all the way.

And as I listen for their voice,
I'll feel Your touch, and make the right choice.

... and at night

Thank you, God, for Your guidance today,
For all the good You sent my way.
In my work and in my play,
Your angels were my strength and stay.

For, each time I listened to their voice,
I felt Your touch, and made the right choice.

—*Linda Staudt Black*

Originally published in the November 9, 1998, issue of the *Christian Science Sentinel*.

To the Sunday School Children

Who sent me the picture depictive of Isaiah xi.

Jesus loves you! so does mother:
   Glad thy Eastertide:
Loving God and one another,
   You in Him abide.
Ours through Him who gave you to us,—
   Gentle as the dove,
Fondling e'en the lion furious,
   Leading kine with love.

Father, in Thy great heart hold them
   Ever thus as Thine!
Shield and guide and guard them; and, when
   At some siren shrine
They would lay their pure hearts' off'ring,
   Light with wisdom's ray—
Beacon beams—athwart the weakly,
   Rough or treacherous way.

Temper every trembling footfall,
   Till they gain at last—
Safe in Science, bright with glory—
   Just the way Thou hast:
Then, O tender Love and wisdom,
   Crown the lives thus blest
With the guerdon of Thy bosom,
   Whereon they may rest!

Pleasant View, Concord, New Hampshire, *April 3, 1899.*

—*Poems, p. 43*

"To the Sunday School Children," by Mary Baker G. Eddy, *Poems*, p. 43.
Originally published in the May 1899, issue of *The Christian Science Journal.*

A Letter to the Children

Pleasant View, Concord, New Hampshire, December 27, 1900.

To the Sunday School Children.

Beloved Children:—It was very lovely in you to remember me on Christmas and send me a pretty pen tray. Among my rare gifts none seemed sweeter than thine. When I saw it I said in my heart I wish I could see those dear children, I wish I knew their sweet faces on the street that I might bow to them, and I hope sometime to see them at our Hall in Concord and address them there.

May the loving Christ still keep you, dear ones, in his arms, and give your young lives love, purity, peace, health, holiness— is the prayer of her who loves you.

Ever yours,
M. B. Eddy.

Courtesy of The Mary Baker Eddy Collection.

A Letter to the Children, by Mary Baker Eddy, January 24, 1901, *Christian Science Sentinel.*

Indexes

Partial Subject Index

Partial Subject Index

Partial Subject Index

Partial Subject Index

Partial Subject Index

Citation Index

Bible verses and citations from the Writings of Mary Baker Eddy
where these children's questions were answered

Citation Index

Citation Index

Citation Index

Citation Index

Notes

Notes

Notes

Notes

Illustrator Bios

When **Danis Collett Mutchler** was a young mother, she frequently illustrated children's articles for the *Christian Science Sentinel*. Often, the article she was asked to illustrate was similar to a recent healing of her own daughter or was one that helped her pray about a current situation. Many of these articles were an important and loved part of her own experience as a mother. She's delighted to see her artwork getting new life in *My Treasury*—some now with color added!

Aside from being an award-winning illustrator, for many years she was also a designer for the *Sentinel* and art director for *The Christian Science Journal*.

These days, Danis lives in a renovated cotton mill in Peterborough, New Hampshire, and is a graphic designer, illustrator, silk painter, and enthusiastic traveler.

Catherine Maria Woolf grew up in Maryland and graduated from University of California, Berkeley with a B.A. in Art History. She worked for a number of years in crafts before finally pursuing her love of art and illustration. Catherine's first published children's book, *My First Hike,* came out in early 2008. She also draws portraits of children.

As a longtime reader of the *Sentinel* and *Journal*, Catherine has always delighted in their illustrations and is very happy to contribute artwork for *My Treasury*.

About Mary Baker Eddy

Mary Baker Eddy, the Discoverer, Founder and Leader of Christian Science, was healed of life-threatening injuries by praying and reading her Bible, including the account in the Gospel of Mark about Christ Jesus healing a man of palsy. Following her healing, she committed her life to understanding how Jesus healed. She explained her discovery of Christian Science in her book, *Science and Health with Key to the Scriptures,* published in 1875. This book has opened the inspired meaning of the Bible to millions. To help spread this message of healing, Mrs. Eddy founded The Church of Christ, Scientist, in 1879, "... to commemorate the word and works of our Master, which should reinstate primitive Christianity and its lost element of healing" (*Church Manual,* p. 17). She began publishing magazines and eventually a newspaper, to enable the Christ-message to reach a wider audience.

For more information about Mary Baker Eddy, please visit
www.marybakereddylibrary.org

Children are welcome in any Christian Science Sunday School. To find a local Sunday School, or to learn more about Christian Science, please visit *www.christianscience.com*. To subscribe to current issues of the *The Christian Science Journal* and *Christian Science Sentinel,* or to purchase a copy of *Science and Health,* please visit *www.spirituality.com*, or your local Christian Science Reading Room. Another resource for children is *My Bible Lesson,* a weekly publication with the Christian Science Bible Lesson displayed in a youthful format.